Singapore Math®
Fact Fluency

2

Author: **Genevieve Collura**
Consultant: **Susan Resnick**

Marshall Cavendish
Education

© 2016 Marshall Cavendish Education Pte Ltd

Published by Marshall Cavendish Education
Times Centre, 1 New Industrial Road, Singapore 536196
Customer Service Hotline: (65) 6213 9444
US Office Tel: 1-800-821-9881
E-mail: tmesales@mceducation.com
Website: www.mceducation.com

First published 2016
Reprinted 2018

ISBN 978-981-4736-35-0

Printed in Singapore

Preface

Singapore Math® Fact Fluency targets two critical elements of mathematical learning—conceptual understanding and fluency. Some activities focus on the understanding of grade-level skills and conceptual standards, while others focus on helping students achieve fluency expectations, resulting in well-balanced practice at every grade level.

Mathematics Standards and Practices

Activities in *Singapore Math® Fact Fluency* align to the Common Core State Standards for Mathematics. At Grade 2, these are:

Operations and Algebraic Thinking
- Represent and solve problems involving addition and subtraction.
- Add and subtract within 20.
- Work with equal groups of objects to gain foundations for multiplication.

Number and Operations in Base Ten
- Understand place value.
- Use place value and properties of operations to add and subtract.

Measurement and Data
- Measure and estimate lengths in standard units.
- Relate addition and subtraction to length.
- Work with time and money.
- Represent and interpret data.

Geometry
- Reason with shapes and their attributes.

Mathematical Practices
MP1. Make sense of problems and persevere in solving them.
MP6. Attend to precision.
MP7. Look for and make use of structure.
MP8. Look for and express regularity in repeated reasoning.

An Emphasis on Instruction

Each practice has been constructed purposefully to guide students from simple number recognition to more advanced conceptual understanding and fluency.

Students can be expected to complete each practice in *Singapore Math® Fact Fluency* in approximately ten minutes, making the practices useful as morning work, class openers, math center or station activities, and as homework.

Activities in the Book

To promote students' mathematical thinking while they build proficiency in calculation, *Singapore Math® Fact Fluency* provides a variety of practices:

 Fact Builder asks students to *apply* specific strategies that promote fluency.

 Fact Strategy Practice asks students to *analyze* problems and *apply* multiple problem-solving strategies.

 Apply and Build Knowledge asks students to *synthesize* and *apply* their knowledge of fact strategies to real-world problems.

 Writing about Math asks students to *evaluate* and *create* new mathematical thinking through movement, drawing, writing, or talking.

 Challenge Questions appear in some practices. These questions help students *acquire readiness* for future learning.

Instructional Support

Additional teacher resources to support this book are available online at http://www.mceducation.us/resources/. These include Timed Mixed Practices, a Diagnostic Assessment, and an Answer Key.

Table of Contents

Chapter 3   Subtraction to 1,000

Chapter 4   Using Bar Models in Addition and Subtraction

Chapter 5   Multiplication and Division

Chapter 6   Multiplication Tables of 2, 5, and 10

Chapter 7   Metric Measurement of Length

Chapter 8   Practicing Facts with Mass

BLANK

1a Number Value

Fill in the blanks.

Hundreds	Tens	Ones

We can understand a number by showing the values of its parts in a place-value chart.

1 The value of 6  is _____.

2 The value of 2 ◰ is _____.

3 The value of 4 ◻ is _____.

4 The number is _____.

Hundreds	Tens	Ones

5 The value of 2 ◰ is _____.

6 The value of 1 ◰ is _____.

7 The value of 8 ◻ is _____.

8 The number is _____.

Hundreds	Tens	Ones

9 The value of 4 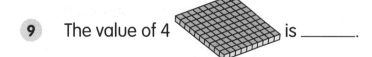 is _____.

10 The value of 3 ▱ is _____.

11 The value of 3 ⬡ is _____.

12 The number is _____.

▰▰▰ = 3 tens   ⬡⬡⬡ = 3 ones

3 ▭ and 3 ⬡ have different values.

Look at the 3s you wrote. Why do they have different values? Use these words to help you answer the question:

different   value   place value   tens   ones

_____

_____

_____

1b Counting On

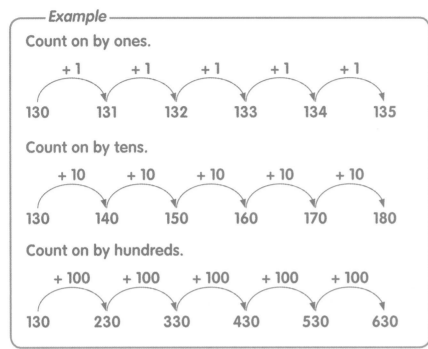

Example

Count on by ones.

+1 +1 +1 +1 +1

130   131   132   133   134   135

Count on by tens.

+10 +10 +10 +10 +10

130   140   150   160   170   180

Count on by hundreds.

+100 +100 +100 +100 +100

130   230   330   430   530   630

Understanding place value helps us count on.

Count on to fill in the blanks. Then circle your answer to complete the sentence.

1

100, _____ , _____ , _____ , _____ , 600

I counted on by: Hundreds   Tens   Ones

2

300, _____ , _____ , _____ , _____ , 350

I counted on by: Hundreds   Tens   Ones

3

240, _____ , _____ , _____ , _____ , 245

I counted on by: Hundreds   Tens   Ones

Example

Hundreds	Tens	Ones

I made the number 524.

Draw tens and ones to make a number.

1

Hundreds	Tens	Ones

I made the number _____.

2

Hundreds	Tens	Ones

I made the number _____.

1d Counting On

Count on to fill in the blanks. Then circle the digit that is different in each number.

1   641, 642, 643, _____ , _____ , _____ , 647

Circle your answer to complete the sentence.

I counted on by: Hundreds   Tens   Ones

2   360, 460, 560, _____ , _____ , _____ , 960

Circle your answer to complete the sentence.

I counted on by: Hundreds   Tens   Ones

3   827, 837, 847, _____ , _____ , _____ , 887

Circle your answer to complete the sentence.

I counted on by: Hundreds   Tens   Ones

How did you know what you were counting on by? Use these words to help you answer the question:

digit   changing   place value

_____

_____

_____

1e Standard Form and Expanded Form

We can write numbers in expanded form to show place values.

┌─ *Example* ─────────────────────────┐
| **Standard Form** **Expanded Form** |
| 246 200 + 40 + 6 |
└─────────────────────────────────────┘

Fill in the blanks.

1 400 + 20 + 3 = _____

2 500 + 30 + 7 = _____

3 672 = _____ + _____ + _____

4 388 = _____ + _____ + _____

5 235 = _____ + _____ + _____

Write three numbers in standard form. Then write them in expanded form.

6 _____ = _____ + _____ + _____

7 _____ = _____ + _____ + _____

8 _____ = _____ + _____ + _____

1f Drawing to Compare

< means "less than."
> means "greater than."
= means "equals."

Example

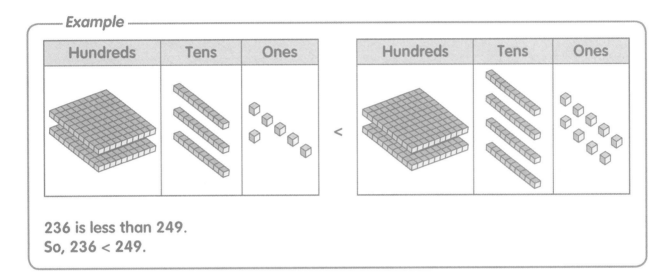

236 is less than 249.
So, 236 < 249.

Fill in the blanks. Then write the correct symbol in the circle.

1

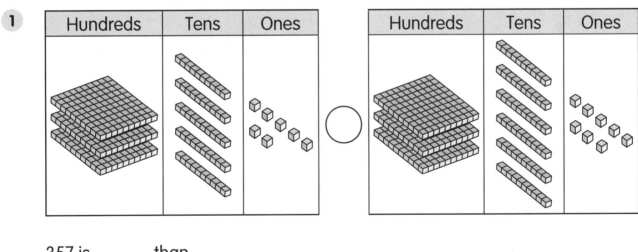

357 is _____ than _____.

So, _____ ◯ _____.

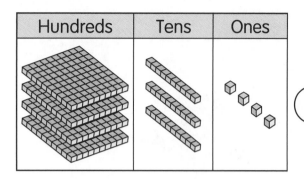

2

Hundreds	Tens	Ones

◯

Hundreds	Tens	Ones

_____ is greater than _____.

So, _____ ◯ _____.

 1g   Counting Back

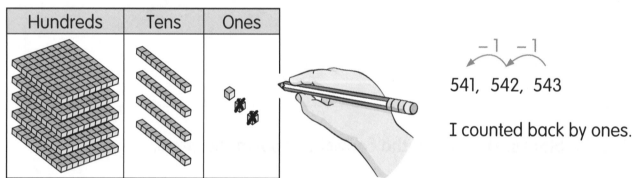

-1 -1

541, 542, 543

I counted back by ones.

Fill in the blanks. Then circle your answer to complete the sentence.

1

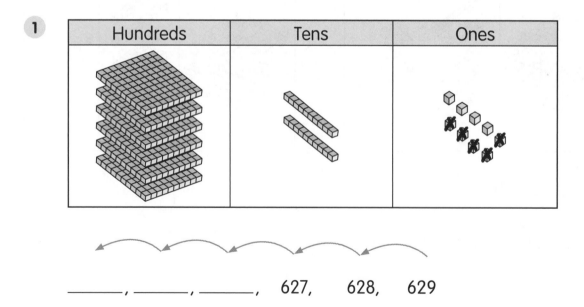

Hundreds	Tens	Ones

_____, _____, _____,   627,   628,   629

I counted back by: Hundreds   Tens   Ones

2

Hundreds	Tens	Ones
		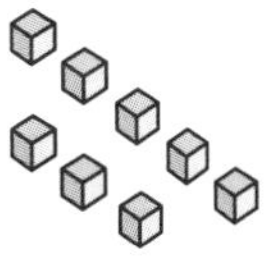

_____, _____, _____, 608, 708, 808

I counted back by: Hundreds   Tens   Ones

3

Hundreds	Tens	Ones
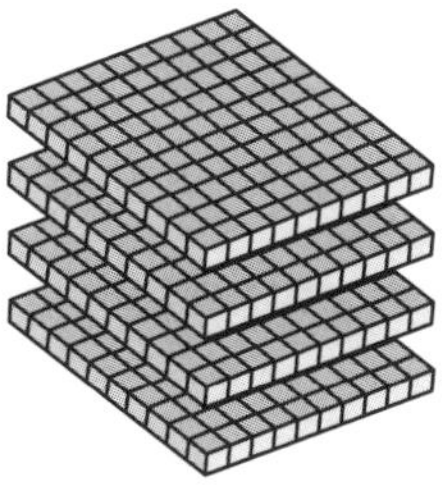	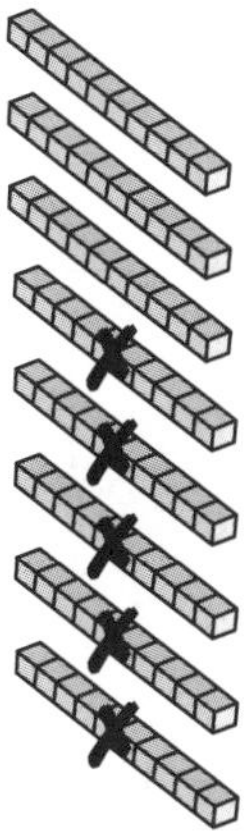	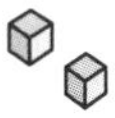

_____, _____, _____, 462, 472, 482

I counted back by: Hundreds   Tens   Ones

1h Counting On and Counting Back

We can count on.

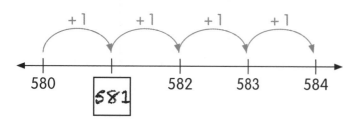

A number line is a tool for finding a missing number in a pattern.

We can count back.

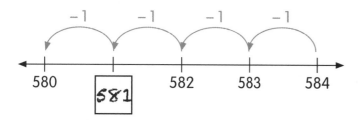

Count on or count back to find the missing numbers on each number line.

1

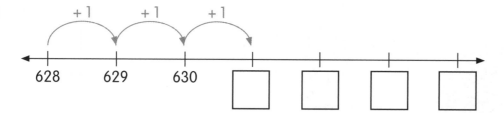

2

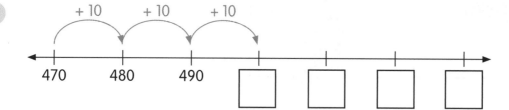

3

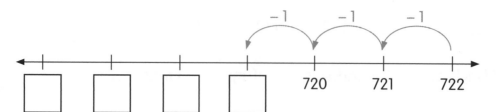

4

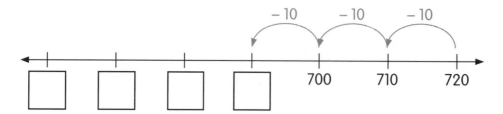

1i   Ordering and Comparing

1   **Order from greatest to least.**

_____, _____, _____

2   **Order from least to greatest.**

_____, _____, _____

3   **Fill in the blanks.**

a.   Make up a set of three numbers.

My numbers are _____, _____, _____.

b.   Exchange numbers with a partner.

My partner's numbers are _____, _____, _____.

c.   Order your partner's numbers from greatest to least. Check each other's work.

From greatest to least, the numbers are _____, _____, _____.

d.   Now order the numbers from least to greatest.

From least to greatest, the numbers are _____, _____, _____.

1j   Counting On and Counting Back

Write the missing numbers in the boxes. Then use the number line to help you fill in the blanks.

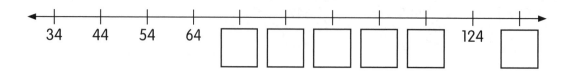

34   44   54   64   ☐   ☐   ☐   ☐   ☐   124   ☐

1   What is 10 more than 94? _____

2   What is 10 less than 54? _____

 3   What is 100 less than 134? _____

1k   Real-World Problems

Use the number line to help you solve the problem.

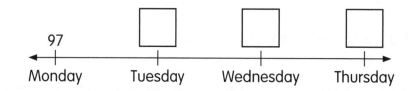

97
Monday   Tuesday   Wednesday   Thursday

Mike asked people to donate toys for a toy drive.

On Monday, Mike had 97 toys. Each day, people gave Mike 10 more toys.

How many toys did Mike have by Thursday? _____

2a   Counting On

$7 + 1 = 8$

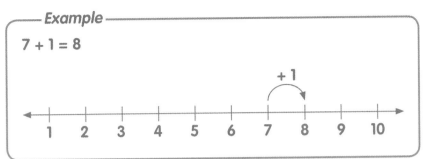

Counting on works best when adding one or two.

Add by counting on.

1 $3 + 2 =$ _____

2 $5 + 1 =$ _____

3 $6 + 2 =$ _____

4 $8 + 1 =$ _____

5 $1 + 2 =$ _____

6 $5 + 2 =$ _____

7 $6 + 1 =$ _____

8 $4 + 2 =$ _____

9 $3 + 1 =$ _____

10 $4 + 1 =$ _____

 2b   Doubles Facts

Add or subtract. Then match the related facts.

1 $5 + 5 =$ _____

2 $8 - 4 =$ _____

3 $4 + 4 =$ _____

4 $4 - 2 =$ _____

5 $3 + 3 =$ _____

6 $10 - 5 =$ _____

7 $2 + 2 =$ _____

8 $6 - 3 =$ _____

9 $1 + 1 =$ _____

10 $2 - 1 =$ _____

2c Adding and Subtracting Zero

Add or subtract.

1. $5 + 0 =$ _____
2. $3 - 0 =$ _____
3. $4 + 0 =$ _____
4. $7 - 0 =$ _____
5. $6 + 0 =$ _____
6. $2 - 0 =$ _____

What do you notice about your answers? Use these words to help you answer the question:

same   number   add   subtract   zero

_____

_____

_____

2d Making Ten

Fill in the missing numbers.

1. _____ $+ 4 = 10$
2. $3 + 7 =$ _____
3. $8 +$ _____ $= 10$
4. $5 +$ _____ $= 10$
5. $1 +$ _____ $= 10$
6. $10 - 7 =$ _____
7. $10 -$ _____ $= 4$
8. _____ $- 2 = 8$
9. $10 -$ _____ $= 1$
10. $10 - 3 =$ _____

2e Counting Back

Counting back works best when subtracting one or two.

Subtract.

1 6 – 1 = _____

2 3 – 2 = _____

3 8 – 2 = _____

4 7 – 1 = _____

5 9 – 2 = _____

6 5 – 1 = _____

7 4 – 1 = _____

8 10 – 1 = _____

9 10 – 2 = _____

10 8 – 1 = _____

 ## 2f Making a Ten

Example

8 + 5 =

(8 + 2) + 3 =

10 + 3 = 15

It is easier to add when you make a ten.

Add the numbers by making a ten.

1 9 + 6 = ?

9 + (1 + 5) = ?

10 + _____ = _____

So, 9 + 6 = _____.

2 8 + 6 = ?

_____ + _____ + 4 = ?

_____ + _____ = _____

So, 8 + 6 = _____.

3   8 + 9 = ?

8 + _____ + _____ = ?

_____ + _____ = _____

So, 8 + 9 = _____.

4   9 + 7 = ?

9 + 1 + _____ = ?

_____ + _____ = _____

So, 9 + 7 = _____.

 2g   **Making a Ten**

Solve mentally by making a ten.

1   7 + 5 = _____

2   5 + 9 = _____

3   6 + 8 = _____

4   8 + 7 = _____

5   9 + 8 = _____

6   5 + 8 = _____

7   7 + 4 = _____

8   7 + 9 = _____

Is it easier for you to count on or make a ten? Use these words to help you explain your answer:

add   count on   ten   easier

_____

_____

_____

_____

2h Doubles Plus One

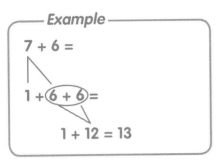

Example

7 + 6 =

1 + ⎝6 + 6⎠ =

1 + 12 = 13

It is easier to add when you use doubles plus one facts.

Use doubles plus one facts to solve.

1 9 + 8 = ?

1 + _____ + 8 = ?

_____ + _____ = _____

So, 9 + 8 = _____.

2 5 + 6 = ?

5 + _____ + 1 = ?

_____ + _____ = _____

So, 5 + 6 = _____.

3 3 + 4 = ?

_____ + _____ + _____ = ?

_____ + _____ = _____

So, 3 + 4 = _____.

4 2 + 3 = ?

_____ + _____ + _____ = ?

_____ + _____ = _____

So, 2 + 3 = _____.

5 4 + 5 = ?

_____ + _____ + _____ = ?

_____ + _____ = _____

So, 4 + 5 = _____.

6 7 + 8 = ?

_____ + _____ + _____ = ?

_____ + _____ = _____

So, 7 + 8 = _____.

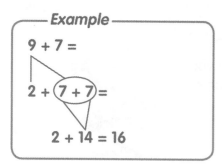

2i Doubles Facts Plus More Than One

Example

9 + 7 =

2 + (7 + 7) =

2 + 14 = 16

You can make a double and add more than just one.

Use doubles facts to solve.

1 8 + 6 = ?

_____ + _____ + 6 = ?

_____ + _____ = _____

So, 8 + 6 = _____.

2 9 + 5 = ?

_____ + _____ + 5 = ?

_____ + _____ = _____

So, 9 + 5 = _____.

3 8 + 5 = ?

_____ + _____ + _____ = ?

_____ + _____ = _____

So, 8 + 5 = _____.

4 9 + 7 = ?

_____ + _____ + _____ = ?

_____ + _____ = _____

So, 9 + 7 = _____.

5 6 + 9 = ?

_____ + _____ + _____ = ?

_____ + _____ = _____

So, 6 + 9 = _____.

6 5 + 7 = ?

_____ + _____ + _____ = ?

_____ + _____ = _____

So, 5 + 7 = _____.

2j Subtracting from Ten, then Adding the Ones

Example

15 – 7 =

(10) + 5 (– 7) =

10 – 7 = 3

3 + the 5 ones that were left over = 8
So, 15 – 7 = 8.

To subtract, first write the greater number as tens and ones. Then subtract the ones from the tens. Finally, add the ones that were left over.

Subtract.

1 14 – 8 = ?

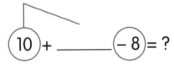

(10) + _____ (– 8) = ?

10 – 8 = _____

_____ + _____ = _____

So, 14 – 8 = _____.

2 18 – 9 = ?

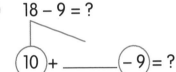

(10) + _____ (– 9) = ?

10 – 9 = _____

_____ + _____ = _____

So, 18 – 9 = _____.

3 16 – 7 = ?

◯ + _____ – ◯ = ?

_____ – _____ = _____

_____ + _____ = _____

So, _____ – _____ = _____.

4 12 – 7 = ?

◯ + _____ – ◯ = ?

_____ – _____ = _____

_____ + _____ = _____

So, _____ – _____ = _____.

5 13 – 5 = ?

_____ + _____ – _____ = ?

_____ – _____ = _____

_____ + _____ = _____

So, _____ – _____ = _____.

6 15 – 6 = ?

_____ + _____ – _____ = ?

_____ – _____ = _____

_____ + _____ = _____

So, _____ – _____ = _____.

2k Addition Using Place Value

Draw base-ten blocks to show an addition problem with two numbers.

The greater number must have hundreds, tens, and ones.
The lesser number must have only tens and ones.

The sum in the ones column must be less than 10.
The sum in the tens column must also be less than 10.

Trade problems with a partner. Solve your partner's problem. Check each other's work.

My problem:

Hundreds	Tens	Ones

+

My bar model for my partner's problem:

21 Addition Without Regrouping

Example

432 + 322 = ?

	Hundreds	Tens	Ones
	4	3	2
+	3	2	2
	7	5	4

7 hundreds 5 tens 4 ones = 754

Use a place-value chart to find each sum. Then fill in the blanks.

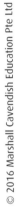

1

	Hundreds	Tens	Ones
	2	4	1
+	1	4	3

_____ hundreds _____ tens _____ ones

2

	Hundreds	Tens	Ones
	5	6	7
+	2	3	1

_____ hundreds _____ tens _____ ones

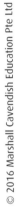

3

Hundreds	Tens	Ones
3	8	8
+ 4	1	1

_____ hundreds   _____ tens   _____ ones

4

Hundreds	Tens	Ones
1	5	3
+ 3	2	5

_____ hundreds   _____ tens   _____ ones

Write the number that goes with each word and picture.

5

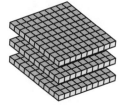

three hundred = _____

6

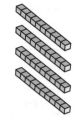

forty = _____

7

nine = _____

8

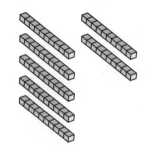

seventy = _____

2m Real-World Addition Problems

Solve. Then fill in the blanks.

1 On Monday, Marla's bowling score was 52. On Tuesday, her score was 47. What was the sum of Marla's bowling scores?

	Hundreds	Tens	Ones
		5	2
+		4	7

The sum of Marla's bowling scores was _____.

2 Ben has 33 lines to learn for the school play. Rebecca has 34 lines to learn. How many lines in all do the two children have to learn?

	Hundreds	Tens	Ones
		3	3
+		3	4

a) Ben and Rebecca have _____ lines in all to learn.

b) How many more lines does Rebecca have to learn than Ben?

Rebecca has _____ more line(s) to learn than Ben.

2n   Addition with Regrouping of Ones

Example

315 + 217 = ?

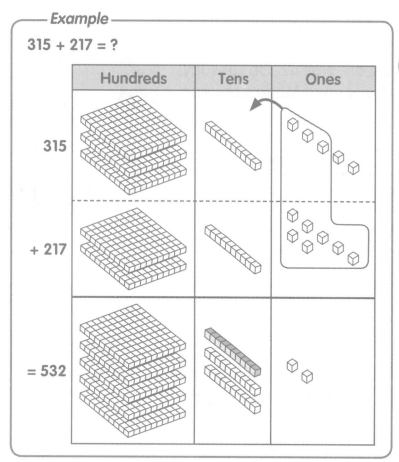

Remember to move the ten after you regroup ones.

Solve. Circle the ten in the ones place to show how you regrouped.

1   22 + 19 = _____

Hundreds	Tens	Ones
+		

2 15 + 17 = _____

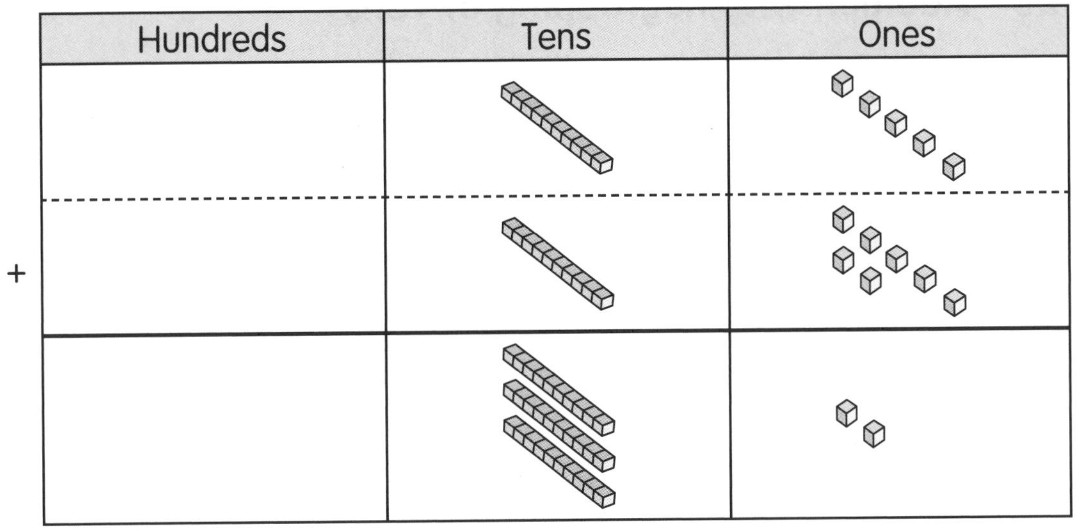

Hundreds	Tens	Ones
+		

3 368 + 215 = _____

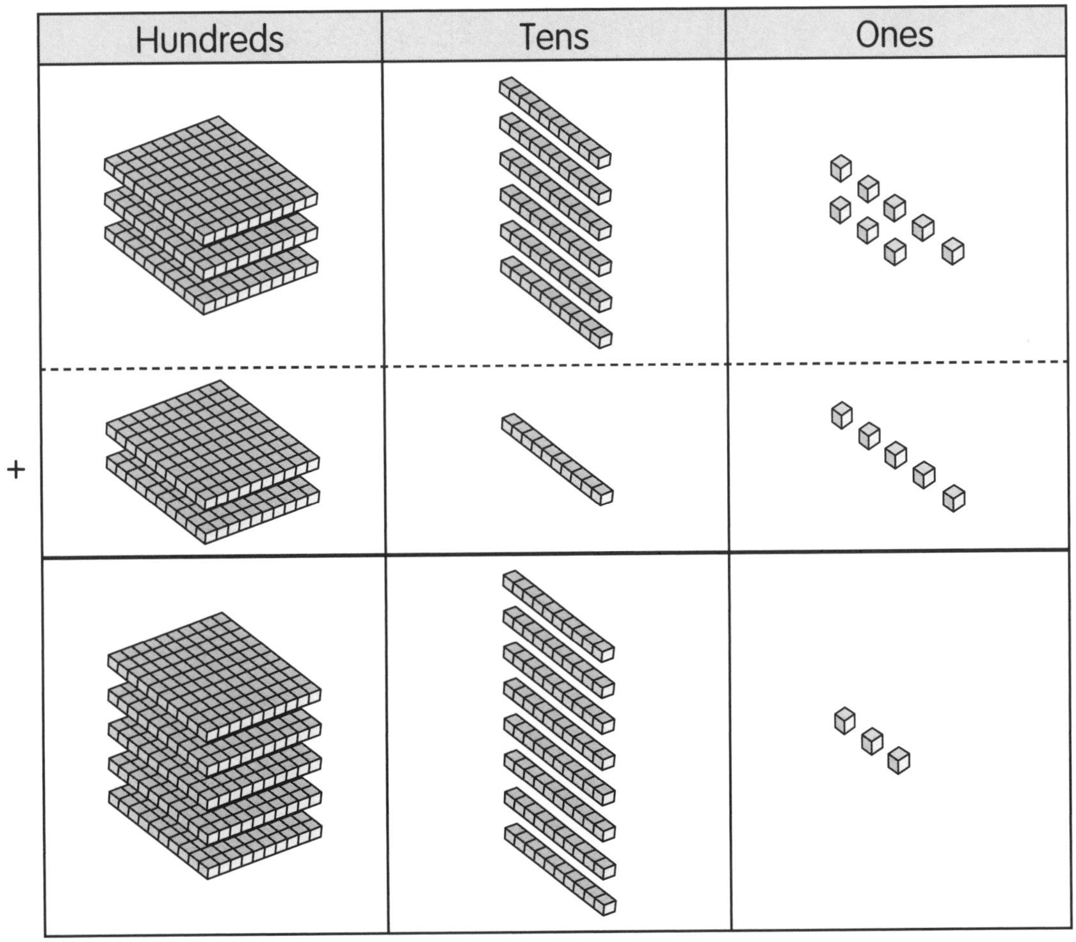

Hundreds	Tens	Ones
+		

2o Addition with Regrouping of Tens

Remember to move the new hundred after you regroup 10 tens.

— *Example* —

325 + 493 = ?

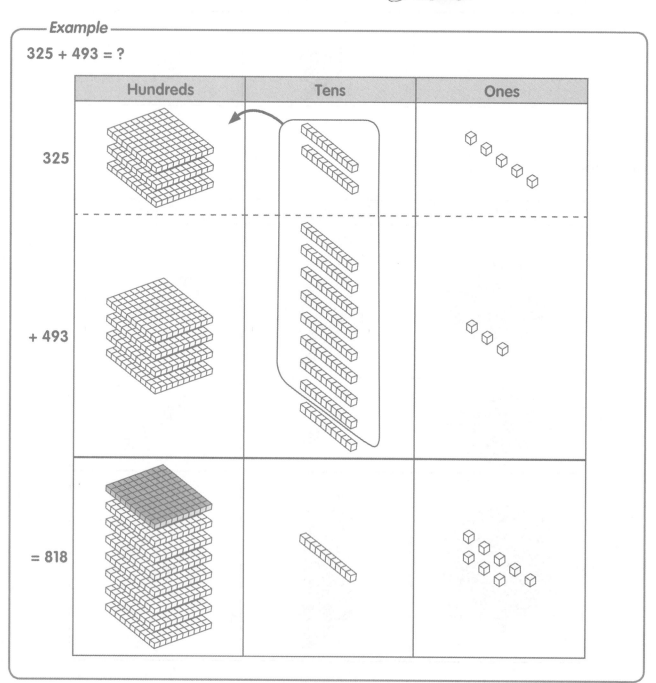

Solve. Circle the hundred in the tens place to show how you regrouped.

1   275 + 564 = _____

Hundreds	Tens	Ones
	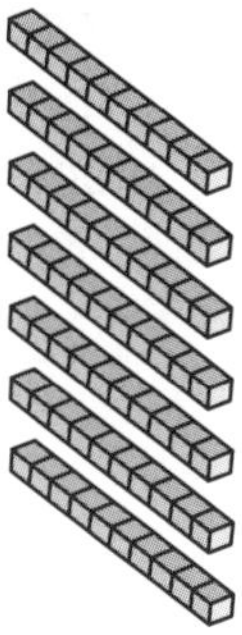	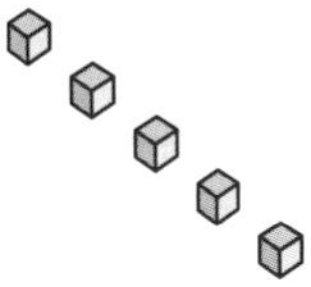
		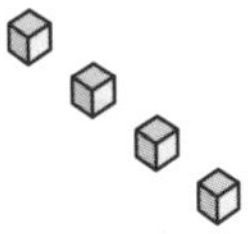
	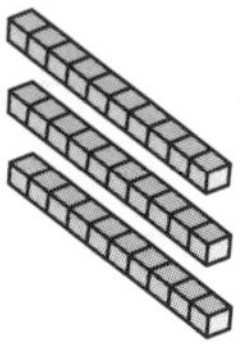	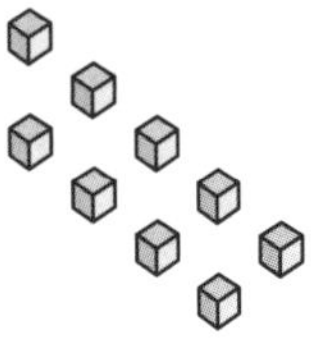

Fill in the blanks.

2   How many tens did you regroup? _____

3   Where did you move the regrouped tens? _____

2p Addition with Regrouping

Example

	Hundreds	Tens	Ones
		1	
+	3	5	7
	4	1	8
	7	7	5

After you regroup, circle the numbers that have the same place value to help you remember to add them all.

Regroup ones to add.

1

	Hundreds	Tens	Ones
	4	5	8
+		2	8

2

	Hundreds	Tens	Ones
	5	7	6
+	2	1	4

Regroup tens to add.

3

	Hundreds	Tens	Ones
	7	9	3
+	1	4	6

4

Hundreds	Tens	Ones
3	9	2
+ 3	7	7

⚙ **Regroup ones and tens to add.**

5

Hundreds	Tens	Ones
6	6	9
+ 2	6	9

6

Hundreds	Tens	Ones
4	5	3
+ 1	7	8

Why do we sometimes regroup to add? Use these words to help you answer the question:

same   digits   regrouping   place value

_____

_____

_____

2q Finding Missing Numbers

Example

3 $\boxed{4}$ 2 + 2 $\boxed{1}$ 3 = 5 $\boxed{5}$ 5

    40 + 10 = 50

4 tens + 1 tens = 5 tens

5 tens – 1 ten = 4 tens
So, the missing number is 1 ten.

Work backwards using fact families to fill in the missing numbers.

1   2 $\boxed{}$ 4 + 4 $\boxed{5}$ 4 = 6 $\boxed{8}$ 8

    _____ + 50 = _____

    _____ tens + 5 tens = 8 tens

2 $\boxed{}$ 3 6 + $\boxed{6}$ 2 2 = $\boxed{9}$ 5 8

    _____ + 600 = _____

    _____ hundreds + 6 hundreds = 9 hundreds

3 5 5 $\boxed{}$ + 1 2 $\boxed{1}$ = 6 7 $\boxed{4}$

    _____ + 1 = _____

    _____ ones + 1 ones = 4 ones

Fill in the missing numbers. Start by adding the ones. Regroup if needed.

4
```
  2 □ 3
+ 6 4 9
───────
  8 6 2
```

5
```
  □ 4 7
+ 2 6 1
───────
  4 □ 8
```

2r Real-World Problems

We can use "keywords" like "more than" and "less than" to help us solve word problems. But they don't always tell if you should add or subtract. So, ask yourself questions to be sure you understand a problem.

Meghan has 432 stamps in her stamp collection. She has 399 fewer stamps than Patrick.

1 **Circle the correct answer.**

a. Who has fewer stamps?   Meghan   Patrick

b. Who has more stamps?   Meghan   Patrick

2 **Solve. Show your work. Then fill in the blank.**

How many stamps does Patrick have?

My work:

Patrick has _____ stamps.

3   Look back at your answer in **1b**. Does your answer match what you found in **2**? Circle your answer.

Yes   No

Does the keyword "fewer" always mean that you should subtract? Use these words to help you answer the question:

less than   fewer   add   subtract   understand   question

_____

_____

3a Subtraction Using Place Value

Example

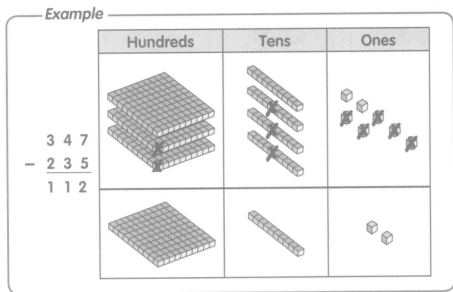

$$\begin{array}{r} 3\ 4\ 7 \\ -\ 2\ 3\ 5 \\ \hline 1\ 1\ 2 \end{array}$$

You can use a base-ten chart to help you subtract.

Cross out base-ten blocks to solve the subtraction problems. Then complete the base-ten chart.

1

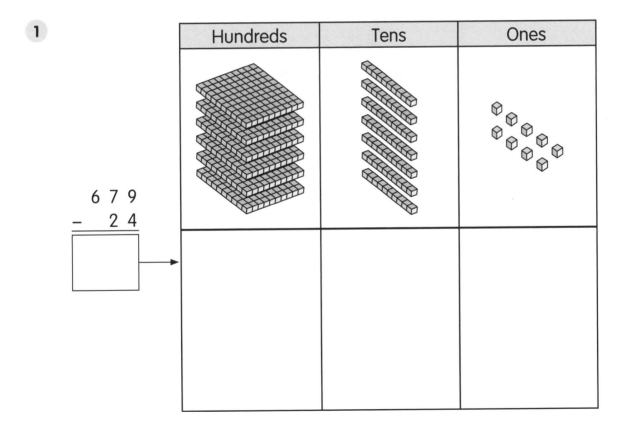

$$\begin{array}{r} 6\ 7\ 9 \\ -\ \ \ 2\ 4 \\ \hline \end{array}$$

2

Hundreds	Tens	Ones

$$\begin{array}{r} 8\ 8\ 8 \\ -\ 1\ 5\ 2 \\ \hline \end{array}$$

3b **Subtraction Using Place Value**

Subtract. Write how many hundreds, tens, and ones are in the difference.

1

Hundreds	Tens	Ones
4	8	5
3	3	1

4 hundreds   8 tens   5 ones

− 3 hundreds   3 tens   1 one

—————————————————————————

_____   _____   _____

2

Hundreds	Tens	Ones
7	9	6
− 2	8	3

7 _____   9 tens   6 _____

−   2 hundreds   8 _____   3 ones

_____

_____   _____   _____

3c   Real-World Problems

1   **Solve. Show your work. Then fill in the blank.**

Brittney had 426 baseball cards. She gave 123 cards to Jose. How many baseball cards does Brittney have now?

My work:

Brittney has _____ baseball cards now.

2   **Write the difference in expanded form.**

a.   _____ = _____ + _____ + _____

b.   The value of the number in the hundreds place is _____.

c.   The value of the number in the tens place is _____.

d.   The value of the number in the ones place is _____.

3d   Regrouping Tens and Ones

Complete the base-ten chart to help you solve the problem. Then fill in the blank.

A worker in a food store stacked 362 cans of soup on a shelf. In one hour, shoppers bought 37 of the cans. How many cans were left on the shelf?

Hundreds	Tens	Ones

_____ cans of soup were left on the shelf.

3e   Checking Subtraction with Addition

Regroup tens or hundreds to solve each problem. Then use addition to check your work.

My work: My check: My work: My check:

1   26
      − 19

2   54
      − 29

3   357
      − 62

4   773
      − 191

3f   Checking Subtraction with Addition

Regroup to subtract. Check your work.

My work: My check:

1   964
         –   57

2   832
         – 491

3   652
         – 397

Tony thinks the difference between 426 and 71 is 455.

4   **Subtract to check Tony's answer. Check your work.**

My work:	My check:

5   **Is Tony's answer correct? Circle your answer.**

Yes   No

3g Finding Missing Numbers

Example

6 – 7 doesn't equal nine, so I must regroup a ten. That means I will have one less ten in the tens place.
So, the tens place started with 9 tens. The missing number is 9. I add to check my thinking:

$$\begin{array}{r} 319 \\ +77 \\ \hline 396 \end{array}$$

Use the example to help you find the missing number in each problem. Check your work.

My work: My check: My work: My check:

1
$$\begin{array}{r} \square\,7 \\ -3\ 8 \\ \hline 3\ 9 \end{array}$$

2
$$\begin{array}{r} 2\ 2 \\ -\ \square\,8 \\ \hline 4 \end{array}$$

3
$$\begin{array}{r} 2\ \square\,5 \\ -2\ 9 \\ \hline 2\ 1\ 6 \end{array}$$

4
$$\begin{array}{r} \square\,5\ 9 \\ -\ 4\ 6\ 2 \\ \hline 1\ 9\ \square \end{array}$$

Explain the steps you follow to solve problems like these. Use these words to help you write:

place value   regroup   backwards   check

First, _____

Next, _____

Then, _____

Finally, _____

3h Subtracting Across Zeros

Regroup to subtract. Check your work.

My work: My check: My work: My check:

1   200
    − 63

2   300
    − 74

3   500
    − 81

4   400
    − 87

5   700
    − 456

6   900
    − 549

Do you change the total value of a number when you regroup? Use these words to help you answer the question:

regroup   change   place value   total   same

_____

_____

_____

Talk about your answer with a partner.

4a Part-Part-Whole Bar Models in Addition

Example

Tina read 5 books this week. Jimmy read 6 books.
How many books did Tina and Jimmy read altogether?

```
      5         6
    Tina      Jimmy
  ┌─────────┬─────────┐
  │         │         │
  └─────────┴─────────┘
            ?
```

The parts are 5 and 6.
You need to add the parts to find the whole.

$$5 + 6 = 11$$

Altogether, Tina and Jimmy read 11 books this week.

> We can use part-part-whole bar models to solve addition and subtraction problems.

Complete the bar model. Solve. Show your work. Then fill in the blank.

Marney has 10 bracelet beads. She buys 27 more. How many beads does Marney have in all?

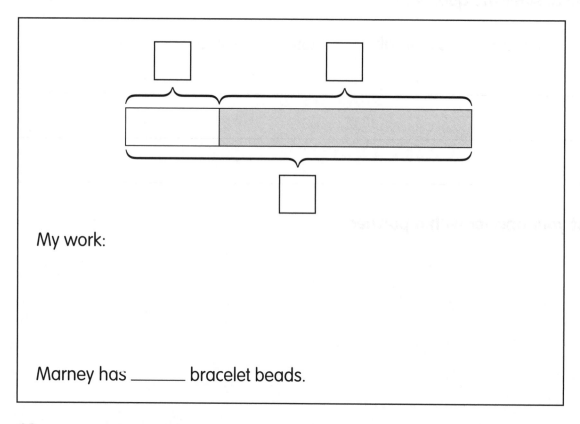

My work:

Marney has _____ bracelet beads.

4b Part-Part-Whole Bar Models in Subtraction

Example

There are 34 oranges for sale. A shopper buys 19 of the oranges. How many oranges are left for sale?

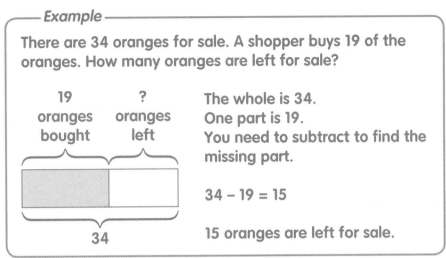

The whole is 34.
One part is 19.
You need to subtract to find the missing part.

34 – 19 = 15

15 oranges are left for sale.

Complete the bar model. Solve. Show your work and check your answer. Then fill in the blank.

Remy bakes 45 loaves of bread for a bake sale. She sells 35 loaves at the sale. How many loaves of bread are left?

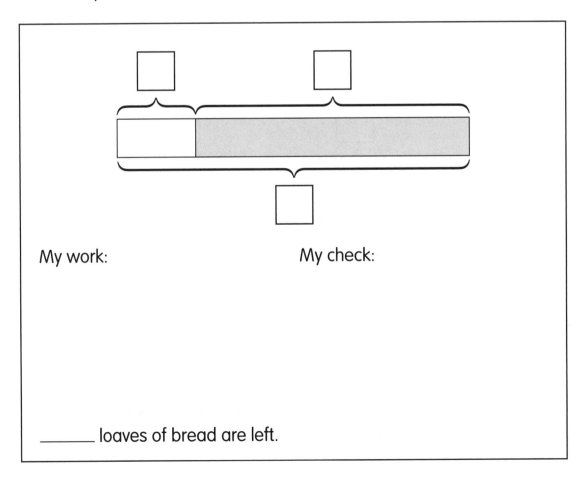

My work: My check:

_____ loaves of bread are left.

4c Part-Part-Whole Bar Models in Addition and Subtraction

Solve. Then label the part-part-whole bar models. Each bar is a whole.

1   15
     + 76

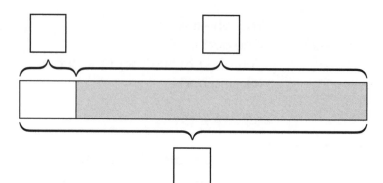

2   137
     + 17

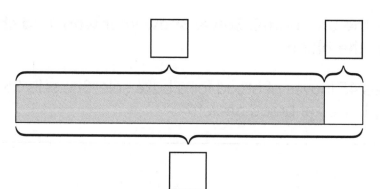

3   25
     − 15

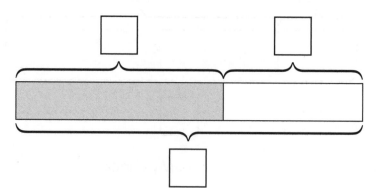

4   989
     − 75

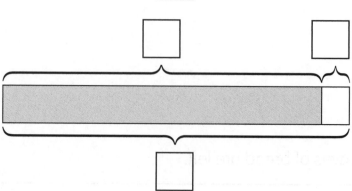

4d Comparison Bar Models in Addition

We can use comparison bar models in addition and subtraction. Comparison bar models compare people, places, or things.

─── *Example* ───

16 boys tried out for the school play.
11 more girls than boys tried out for the play.
How many girls tried out for the play?

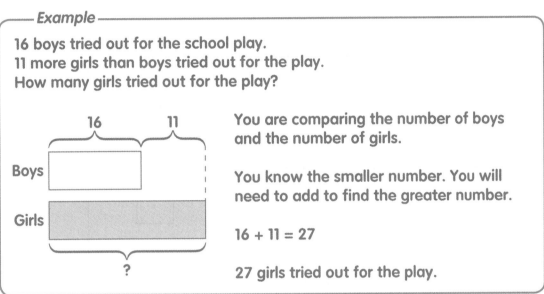

You are comparing the number of boys and the number of girls.

You know the smaller number. You will need to add to find the greater number.

16 + 11 = 27

27 girls tried out for the play.

Complete the bar model. Solve. Show your work. Then fill in the blank.

Bonnie has 465 books in her library. Chelsea has 27 more books than Bonnie. How many books does Chelsea have?

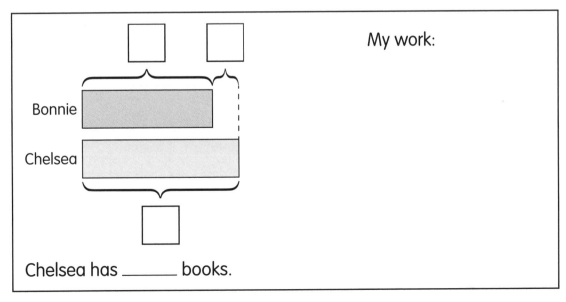

My work:

Chelsea has _____ books.

4e Comparison Bar Models in Subtraction

Complete the bar model. Solve. Show your work and check your answer. Then fill in the blank.

There are 826 toys in bucket A. Bucket B has 97 fewer toys than bucket A. How many toys does bucket B have?

Bucket _____

Bucket _____

My work:

My check:

Bucket B has _____ toys.

4f **Comparison Bar Models in Addition**

Complete the bar model. Solve. Show your work. Then fill in the blank.

Raoul is an artist. He painted a picture on a wall
64 ft long. Sara is also an artist. She painted
a picture on a wall 29 ft longer than Raoul's wall.
How long is Sara's painting?

My work:

Sara's painting is _____ ft long.

4g   Comparison Bar Models in Subtraction

**Complete the bar model. Solve. Show your work and check your answer.
Then fill in the blank.**

677 students were at the aquarium on Tuesday. 35 fewer students were
there on Wednesday. How many students were at the aquarium on Wednesday?

My work: My check:

There were _____ students at the aquarium on Wednesday.

4h Part-Part-Whole Bar Models

Draw a part-part-whole bar model to help you solve each problem.

1
$$\begin{array}{r} 55 \\ -\ 29 \\ \hline \end{array}$$

2
$$\begin{array}{r} 45 \\ +\ 48 \\ \hline \end{array}$$

4i Addition and Subtraction Problems

You can use more than one bar model to solve two-step problems. You can use different kinds of bar models, too.

Solve each part of the problem.

1 Maya and her friends Pedro, Laura, and Mike live in the same apartment building. On Monday, Maya climbed 27 stairs from her apartment to visit Pedro. She climbed 67 more stairs to get to Laura's apartment. How many stairs are there between Maya's and Laura's apartments?

What kind of bar model will you draw to solve this part of the problem? Circle your answer.

Part-part-whole   Comparison

Draw a bar model to help you solve. Show your work. Then fill in the blank.

My bar model: My work:

There are _____ stairs between Laura's and Maya's apartments.

2 On Tuesday, Maya went to visit Mike. She climbed 35 stairs fewer than she did on Monday. How many stairs did Maya climb to visit Mike?

What kind of bar model will you draw to solve this part of the problem? Circle your answer.

Part-part-whole   Comparison

Solve. Show your work and check your answer. Then fill in the blank.

My bar model:

My work: My check:

Maya climbed _____ stairs to visit Mike.

4j   Addition and Subtraction Problems

Write a problem. Trade problems with a partner. Draw a bar model to help you solve your partner's problem. Check each other's work.

My problem:

_____

_____

_____

My bar model for my partner's problem:

My work:

5a Multiplication as Repeated Addition

Example

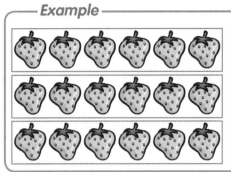

Repeated addition:
6 + 6 + 6 = 18

Multiplication:
3 × 6 = 18

You can use repeated addition to help you multiply.

Use the pictures to help you add and multiply. Fill in the blanks.

 1

_____ + _____ = _____

_____ × _____ = _____

2

_____ + _____ = _____

_____ × _____ = _____

 3

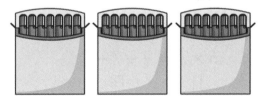

_____ + _____ + _____ = _____

_____ × _____ = _____

 4

_____ + _____ + _____ = _____

_____ × _____ = _____

5b Grouping in Multiplication

Example

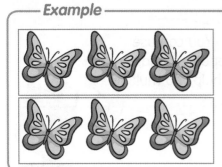

2 groups of 3 butterflies
= 6 butterflies

Multiplication:
$2 \times 3 = 6$

The words "groups of" tell you to multiply.

Circle the groups in each picture. Then fill in the blanks.

1

_____ groups of 5 = _____

_____ × _____ = _____

2

_____ groups of 9 = _____

_____ × _____ = _____

5c Relating Addition to Multiplication

Multiply to find each product. Add to find each sum.
Are the product and sum equal? Circle Yes or No.

1 $2 \times 4 = 4 + 4$

_____   _____

Yes   or   No

2 $5 \times 7 = 7 + 7 + 7$

_____   _____

Yes   or   No

3 $2 \times 6 = 6 + 6 + 6$

_____   _____

Yes   or   No

4 $3 \times 8 = 8 + 8 + 8 + 8$

_____   _____

Yes   or   No

5d Multiplying by Zero

Example

3 × 0 means 3 groups of zero.
This is the same as 0 + 0 + 0.

When you multiply by zero, the product is always zero.

Fill in the blanks.

1. 5 × 0 means _____ groups of _____.

    5 × 0 = _____

2. 9 × 0 means the same as _____ + _____ + _____ + _____ + _____ +

    _____ + _____ + _____ + _____

    9 × 0 = _____

3. 4 × 0 means _____ groups of _____.

    4 × 0 = _____

4. 10 × 0 means the same as _____ + _____ + _____ + _____ + _____ +

    _____ + _____ + _____ + _____ + _____

    10 × 0 = _____

5. 0 × 5 means _____ groups of _____.

    0 × 5 = _____

6. 6 × 0 = _____

7. 8 × 0 = _____

8. 7 × 0 = _____

9. 0 × 4 = _____

10. 0 × 0 = _____

11. 0 × 9 = _____

5e Multiplying by 1

> **Example**
>
> 4×1 means the same as 4 groups of 1.
>
>
>
> 4 groups of 1 = 4
> So, $4 \times 1 = 4$.

The product of any number and 1 is the number itself.

Draw a picture to help you solve each problem.

1 $5 \times 1 = $ _____

2 $1 \times 7 = $ _____

3 $9 \times 1 = $ _____

4 $1 \times 4 = $ _____

5 $6 \times 1 = $ _____

6 $1 \times 9 = $ _____

5f   Division

Example

$8 \div 4 = 2$ means that 8 is the whole that we are dividing into 4 equal groups.
There are 2 equal parts in each group.

When you divide, you find equal parts of a whole.

Fill in the blanks.

1   There are _____ puppies in all.

   So, the whole is _____.

2   Draw circles around each group of 2 puppies.

   You divided the whole into _____ groups.

3   There are _____ puppies in each group.

4   Write the division problem and the answer.

   _____ ÷ _____ = _____

5g Division as Repeated Subtraction

You can use repeated subtraction to help you divide.

Example

A pet shop owner has 20 fish. She puts the fish in bags of water. She puts 4 fish in each bag. How many bags does the pet shop owner use?

$20 \div 4 = 5$ bags of fish

$20 - 4 - 4 - 4 - 4 - 4 = 0$

Use the pictures to help you fill in the blanks.

1

$15 \div \underline{\hspace{1cm}} = \underline{\hspace{1cm}}$

$15 - \underline{\hspace{1cm}} - \underline{\hspace{1cm}} - \underline{\hspace{1cm}} = \underline{\hspace{1cm}}$

2

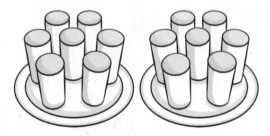

$\underline{\hspace{1cm}} \div \underline{\hspace{1cm}} = \underline{\hspace{1cm}}$

$\underline{\hspace{1cm}} - \underline{\hspace{1cm}} - \underline{\hspace{1cm}} = \underline{\hspace{1cm}}$

5h Relating Subtraction to Division

You can use fact families to solve tricky questions.

Fill in the blanks.

1 Use a fact family to solve the problem.

$0 \div 4 =$ _____

2 Write the fact that helped you find the answer.

_____ × _____ = _____

3 Use repeated subtraction to check your answer.

$0 -$ _____ $-$ _____ $-$ _____ $-$ _____ $=$ _____

4 Complete the sentence.

0 divided by a whole number always equals _____.

5 Write two new division problems with zero as the answer.

$0 \div$ _____ $= 0$

$0 \div$ _____ $= 0$

5i Real-World Multiplication and Division Problems

Fill in the blanks.

1 Four students are playing ring toss at a school fair. Each student has 6 rings to toss. How many rings do the students have in all?

_____ + _____ + _____ + _____ = _____

_____ × _____ = _____

The students have _____ rings in all.

2 Bernie has a new piggy bank. He puts 7 cents in his piggy bank each day. How many days will it take Bernie to save 35 cents?

_____ ÷ _____ = _____

35 – _____ – _____ – _____ – _____ – _____ = _____

It will take Bernie _____ days to save 35 cents.

3 Linda has 12 bottle caps. She gives 2 bottle caps to each of her playmates until she has none left. How many of Linda's playmates receive bottle caps?

_____ ÷ _____ = _____

12 – _____ – _____ – _____ – _____ – _____ – _____ = _____

_____ of Linda's playmates receive bottle caps.

6a   Drawing Groups of 2

Example

3 groups of 2 = 6

3 × 2 = 6

You can draw groups of objects to help you multiply.

Draw groups of squares to help you multiply.

1

2 groups of 2 = _____

2 × 2 = _____

2

6 groups of 2 = _____

6 × 2 = _____

3

4 groups of 2 = _____

4 × 2 = _____

4

2 groups of 5 = _____

5 × 2 = _____

6b Skip-Counting by 2s

You can skip-count
to help you multiply.

Use skip-counting to help you multiply.

1   3 × 2 = _____

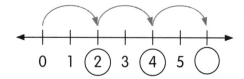

2, 4, _____

2   4 × 2 = _____

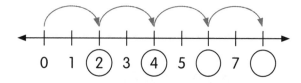

2, 4, _____, _____

3   7 × 2 = _____

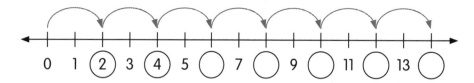

2, _____, _____, _____, _____, _____, _____

4   9 × 2 = _____

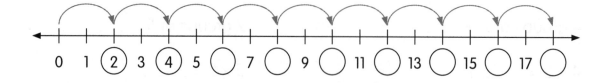

_____, _____, _____, _____, _____, _____, _____, _____, _____

6c Using Dot Grids in Multiplication

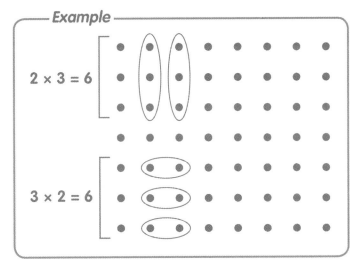

Example

$2 \times 3 = 6$

$3 \times 2 = 6$

You can multiply the same numbers in either order and get the same product.

Use the dot grids to help you multiply.

1    $8 \times 2 =$ _____

      $2 \times 8 =$ _____

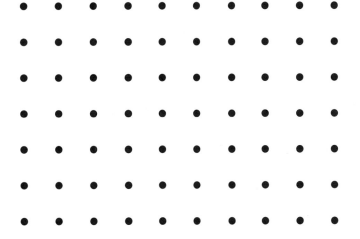

2    $5 \times 2 =$ _____

      $2 \times 5 =$ _____

6d Working with 10 in Multiplication

Example

7 groups of 2 = 5 groups of 2 + 2 groups of 2

5 groups of 2 is the same as 5 × 2.

2 groups of 2 is the same as 2 × 2.

5 × 2 + 2 × 2

⬇   ⬇

10   +   4 = 14

So, 7 × 2 = 14

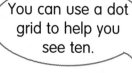

You can use a dot grid to help you see ten.

Use the dot grids to help you multiply. Circle the 2s that make up the ten. Then box the 2s that make up the ones.

1   8 groups of 2 = 5 groups of 2 + 3 groups of 2

5 × 2 = _____ + 3 × 2 = _____

_____   +   _____ = _____

8 × 2 = _____

2 9 groups of 2 = 5 groups of 2 + 4 groups of 2

$$5 \times 2 = \text{_____} + 4 \times 2 = \text{_____}$$

$$\text{_____} + \text{_____} = \text{_____}$$

$9 \times 2 = \text{_____}$

• • • • • • • • •

• • • • • • • • •

• • • • • • • • •

• • • • • • • • •

• • • • • • • • •

• • • • • • • • •

• • • • • • • • •

6e Showing Equal Values

Use facts you know to find the missing numbers.

1 $7 \times 2 = 10 + \text{_____}$

_____ _____

2 $6 \times 2 = 10 + \text{_____}$

_____ _____

3 $8 \times 2 = 20 - \text{_____}$

_____ _____

4 $7 \times 2 = 20 - \text{_____}$

_____ _____

6f Working with 20 in Multiplication

Use the dot grid to help you see 20. Cross out the groups you subtract to get the answer.

1

9×2 = 10 groups of 2 – _____ group(s) of 2

⬇   ⬇

_____ – _____ = _____

So, $9 \times 2 =$ _____.

2

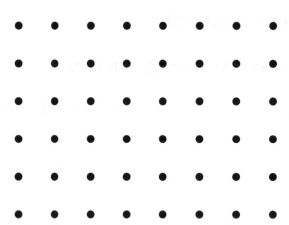

8×2 = 10 groups of 2 – _____ group(s) of 2

⬇   ⬇

_____ – _____ = _____

So, $8 \times 2 =$ _____.

6g Real-World Multiplication Problems

Use the dot grids to help you find the answers. Then fill in the blanks.

1   Daniel bought 7 goldfish. Each goldfish cost $2. How much did Daniel pay for 7 goldfish?

_____ × _____ = $_____

Daniel paid $_____ for 7 goldfish.

2   Marinella bought 6 shirts at a sale. Each shirt cost $5. How much did Marinella pay for all the shirts?

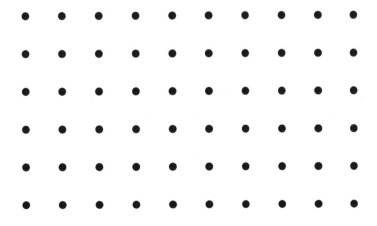

_____ × _____ = $_____

Marinella paid $_____ for 6 shirts.

6h   Skip-Counting by 5s

Start at 5 and skip-count by 5s. Shade each number you count. Read each number aloud with a partner.

1	2	3	4	5	6	7	8	9	10
11	12	13	14	15	16	17	18	19	20
21	22	23	24	25	26	27	28	29	30
31	32	33	34	35	36	37	38	39	40
41	42	43	44	45	46	47	48	49	50
51	52	53	54	55	56	57	58	59	60
61	62	63	64	65	66	67	68	69	70
71	72	73	74	75	76	77	78	79	80
81	82	83	84	85	86	87	88	89	90
91	92	93	94	95	96	97	98	99	100

Look at the shaded numbers in the chart. What do you notice about them? Use these words to help you answer the question:

five   ten   ones   tens   place

_____

_____

_____

6i Skip-Counting by 5s

Example

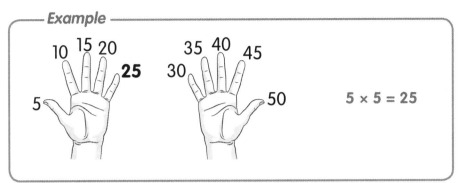

$$5 \times 5 = 25$$

Use your hands to help you multiply.

1 $5 \times 6 = $ _____

2 $4 \times 5 = $ _____

3 $9 \times 5 = $ _____

4 $7 \times 5 = $ _____

5 $3 \times 5 = $ _____

6 $5 \times 2 = $ _____

7 $8 \times 5 = $ _____

8 $5 \times 5 = $ _____

 6j   Using Dot Grids in Multiplication

Circle groups of dots to help you multiply.

1 $7 \times 5 = $ _____

2 $9 \times 5 = $ _____

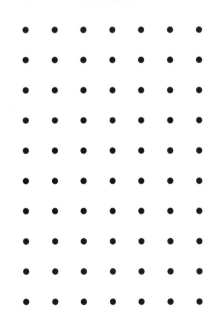

6k Using Place Value in Multiplication

Example

Knowing that $1 \times 5 = 5$ helps us to know that $10 \times 5 = 50$.

Knowing simple multiplication facts helps us understand other multiplication facts.

Use multiplication facts to help you solve.

1 $1 \times 3 = $ _____, so $10 \times 3 = $ _____

2 $6 \times 1 = $ _____, so $6 \times 10 = $ _____

3 $1 \times 4 = $ _____, so $10 \times 4 = $ _____

4 $5 \times 1 = $ _____, so $5 \times 10 = $ _____

5 $1 \times 2 = $ _____, so $10 \times 2 = $ _____

What did you observe when you multiplied a number by 1 and then multiplied the same number by 10? Use these words to help you answer the question:

zero   ten   one   multiply

_____

_____

_____

_____

6l **Using Dot Grids in Multiplication**

Work with a partner. Follow the instructions. Then fill in the blanks.

Partner 1:

Circle 4 groups of 5. Then use your work to complete the number sentence.

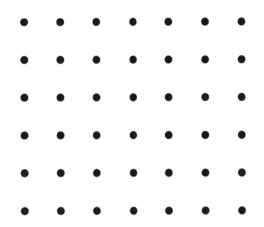

_____ groups of _____ = _____

Partner 2:

Circle 5 groups of 4. Then use your work to complete the number sentence.

_____ groups of _____ = _____

Answer the questions below.

1   Compare your dot grids. Are they the same or different?

_____

2   Compare your number sentences. Are the answers the same or different?

_____

3   Explain your answers in **1** and **2**.

_____

_____

_____

6m Multiplying by 10

Use the dot grid or skip-count to help you multiply by 10.

1. 10 × _____ = 50

2. 6 × 10 = _____

3. 10 × _____ = 90

4. 4 × 10 = _____

5. 10 × 3 = _____

6. _____ × 10 = 10

7. 10 × 7 = _____

8. 10 × _____ = 20

6n   Odd and Even Numbers

Example

You can put an even number of objects into groups of 2. 4 is an example of an even number.

You cannot put an odd number of objects into groups of 2. 3 is an example of an odd number.

You can make groups of 2 to figure out if a number is even or odd.

Circle groups of 2. Write if the total number of squares in each item is even or odd.

1      _____

2      _____

3      _____

4      _____

5      _____

6      _____

6o   Even and Odd Numbers

Add. Then write if the sum is odd or even.

1   1 + 7 = _____   _____

2   4 + 3 = _____   _____

3   6 + 6 = _____   _____

4   3 + 0 = _____   _____

5   8 + 2 = _____   _____

6   2 + 3 = _____   _____

7   7 + 4 = _____   _____

8   9 + 7 = _____   _____

9   8 + 5 = _____   _____

10   0 + 15 = _____   _____

6p   Real-World Multiplication Problems

Solve. Then fill in the blanks.

1   Tristan has 6 bundles of straws to use for an art project. There are 10 straws in each bundle. How many straws are there in all?

_____ × _____ = _____

There are _____ straws in all.

2   Alexa has 5 bags of marbles. There are 8 marbles in each bag. How many marbles does Alexa have?

_____ × _____ = _____

Alexa has _____ marbles in all.

7a Real-World Length Problems (Meters)

Solve. Show your work and check your answer. Then fill in the blank.

Tower A is 45 m tall. Tower B is 82 m tall. How much taller is Tower B than Tower A?

> **Meter** is a unit of measure. We use meters to measure the length of long objects and short distances. We use the letter "m" to stand for the word "meter."

My work: My check:

Tower B is _____ m taller than Tower A.

 ## 7b Real-World Length Problems (Meters)

Solve. Show your work. Then fill in the blank.

Marlin has a rope 11 m long. He uses the rope to make a triangle. Each side of the triangle is 1 m long. How much rope does Marlin have left over? You may draw a picture or bar model to help you find the answer.

My work:

Marlin has _____ m of rope left over.

7c Real-World Length Problems (Centimeters)

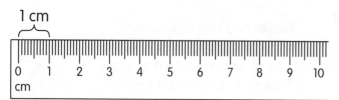

1 cm

0 1 2 3 4 5 6 7 8 9 10
cm

Centimeter is a unit of measure. We use centimeters to measure the length of short objects. We use the letters "cm" to stand for the word "centimeter."

Solve. Show your work. Then fill in the blank.

1   Kayden and his dad put up a shelf 354 cm long. They put up another shelf 266 cm long. How long are the two shelves when they are put together?

My work:

Together, the shelves are _____ cm long.

2   Kayden and his dad put up a third shelf 280 cm long. How long are the three shelves when they are put together?

My work:

Together, the shelves are _____ cm long.

7d Using Bar Models in Length Problems (Meters)

Draw a bar model to help you solve. Show your work and check your answer.

Ricardo walked 189 m to the playground. Janice walked 342 m to the playground. How many more meters did Janice walk than Ricardo? Draw a bar model to help you find the answer.

My bar model:

My work: My check:

Janice walked _____ m more than Ricardo.

7e Using Bar Models in Length Problems (Centimeters)

Draw a bar model to help you solve. Show your work and check your answer. Then fill in the blank.

Dora bought 84 cm of fabric. She cut the fabric into three pieces. One piece is 29 cm long. Another piece is 38 cm long. How long is the third piece of fabric?

My bar model:

My work: My check:

The third piece of fabric is _____ cm long.

7f Real-World Length Problems

Write a math problem that uses centimeters or meters. Choose the unit of measurement that fits your problem better.

_____

_____

_____

Trade problems with a partner. Solve your partner's problem. Discuss your work when you have both finished.

My bar model for my partner's problem:

My work:

7g   Using Bar Models in Length Problems

Draw a bar model to help you solve. Show your work. Then fill in the blank.

A kangaroo hopped 99 m to a bush. Then she hopped 212 more meters to another bush. How many meters did the kangaroo hop in all?

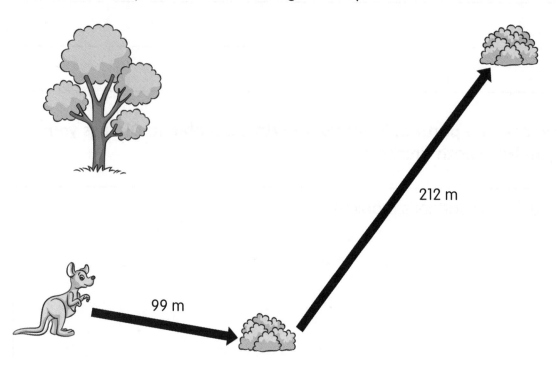

My bar model:

My work:

The kangaroo hopped _____ m in all.

7h   Checking Subtraction and Addition

Solve each problem. Then check your work.

My work: My check:

1   22 cm + 563 cm =

2   910 cm + 35 cm =

3   827 cm − 442 cm =

4   192 m − 57 m =

 7i   The Importance of Facts

Martina found this note from her little brother
in her lunchbox. Use these words to help Martina
write an answer to her little brother's question:

Why is it
important for
me to practice
my facts when I
solve a problem?

easier   important   add   subtract   know   different   ways

_____

_____

_____

_____

8a   Real-World Mass Problems (Kilograms)

Kilogram is a unit of measure. We use kilograms to measure the mass of heavy objects. We use the letters "kg" to stand for the word "kilogram."

Use the measurements to answer the questions.

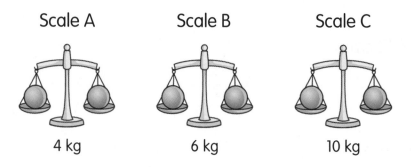

Scale A   Scale B   Scale C

4 kg   6 kg   10 kg

Each scale in the picture is balanced. This means that the mass of the balls on each scale is the same.

1   What is the mass of each ball on Scale A? _____ kg

2   What is the mass of each ball on Scale B? _____ kg

3   What is the mass of each ball on Scale C? _____ kg

4   Explain how you solved each problem.

_____

_____

_____

_____

8b   Mass

Solve.

Each of these empty suitcases has a mass of 3 kg.

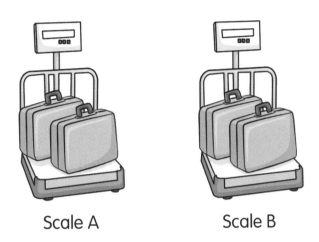

Scale A   Scale B

1   What is the mass of two suitcases? _____ kg

2   What is the total mass of the four suitcases? _____ kg

What did you do to find the total mass of the suitcases? Circle your answer.

I used doubles facts.   I multiplied.

Explain why you did it this way.

I did it this way because _____

_____

_____

_____

8c Real-World Mass Problems (Kilograms)

Solve.

Horse A

389 kg

Horse B

427 kg

My work: My check:

1 What is the total mass of
Horse A and Horse B?

2 How much heavier is
Horse B than Horse A?

8d Mass

**Pretend that the mass of each ball on the scale is either
2 kg or 5 kg. Use these words and the mass you choose
to write a multiplication problem:**

kg   each   group   scale   how many   in all

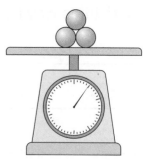

_____

_____

_____

8e Real-World Mass Problems (Grams)

Gram is a unit of measure.
We use grams to measure
the mass of light objects.
We use the letter "g" to stand
for the word "gram."

Draw a bar model to help you solve. Show your work and check your answer. Then fill in the blank.

How much heavier is the broccoli than the orange?

orange
165 g

broccoli
542 g

My bar model:

My work: My check:

The broccoli is _____ g heavier than the orange.

Draw an object on each scale and write its mass. Use your pictures to write an addition or subtraction problem.

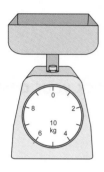 Mass = _____

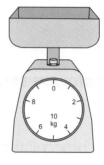 Mass = _____

Use these words to help you write your problem.

kg   g   mass   scale   together   more   less   in all

My problem:

_____

_____

_____

Trade problems with a partner. Draw a bar model to solve your partner's problem. Discuss your work when you both have finished.

My bar model for my partner's problem:	My work:

9a Volume and Multiplication

> The volume of a container is how much liquid it can hold. We use **liters** to measure volume. We use the letter "L" to stand for the word "liter."

Solve. Draw a picture or a bar model to help you find the answer.

1 A restaurant owner has 4 large pitchers. Each pitcher can hold 2 L of juice. How many liters of juice can the 4 pitchers hold?

My picture/bar model:

Fill in the blanks to show two ways to find the answer.

2 Repeated addition sentence:

_____ + _____ + _____ + _____ = _____

3 Multiplication sentence:

_____ × _____ = _____

The 4 pitchers can hold _____ L of juice.

9b   Volume and Division

Solve. Draw a picture or a bar model to help you find the answer.

1   A gardener has some buckets. The buckets hold 15 L of water in all. Each bucket holds 3 L of water. How many buckets does the gardener have?

My picture/bar model:

Fill in the blanks to show two ways to find the answer.

2   Repeated subtraction sentence:

15 – _____ – _____ – _____ – _____ – _____ = _____

3   Division sentence:

_____ ÷ _____ = _____

There are _____ L of water in each bucket.

9c Real-World Volume Problems

Draw a bar model to help you solve. Show your work. Then fill in the blank.

Melissa has 2 large cans of oil. One can holds 6 L, and the other holds 4 L.
How many liters of oil does Melissa have altogether?

My bar model: My work:

Melissa has _____ L of oil altogether.

What kind of bar model did you draw? Circle your answer.

Part-part-whole   Comparison

9d Real-World Volume Problems

**Draw a bar model to help you solve. Show your work and check your answer.
Then fill in the blank.**

At the beach, Liana filled a bucket with 20 L of water. The bucket became too heavy,
so Liana emptied 17 L back into the ocean. How many liters of water did the bucket
hold afterward?

My bar model: My work: My check:

The bucket held _____ L of water afterward.

9e Real-World Volume Problems

Draw a bar model to help you solve. Show your work. Then fill in the blank.

Winston's Juice Store had 78 L of apple juice for sale. On Thursday, the owner sold 18 L of apple juice. On Friday, she sold 37 L of apple juice. How many liters of apple juice did the owner sell altogether on Thursday and Friday?

My bar model: My work:

The owner sold _____ L of apple juice altogether.

9f Real-World Volume Problems

Read the problem in 9e again. Draw a bar model to help you solve the problem below. Show your work and check your answer. Then fill in the blank.

How much apple juice did the owner of Winston's Juice Store have left, after her total sales on Thursday and Friday?

My bar model: My work: My check:

The owner had _____ L of apple juice left.

9g Volume and Addition

Fill in the blanks.

Milan bought 6 L of juice for a party. He wants to pour the juice into 3 large bottles like these. Each bottle can hold up to 4 L.

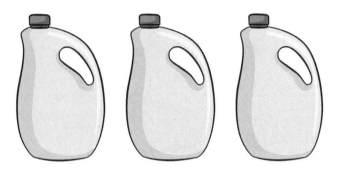

Show three different ways Milan can use the bottles to carry 6 L of juice.

1 _____ L + _____ L + _____ L = 6 L

2 _____ L + _____ L + _____ L = 6 L

3 _____ L + _____ L + _____ L = 6 L

Show two ways Milan can use only two of the bottles to carry 6 L of juice.

4 _____ L + _____ L = 6 L

5 _____ L + _____ L = 6 L

10a   Finding the Sum

Solve.

1. 92
    + 28

2. 36
    + 42

3. 158
    + 59

4. 361
    + 35

5. 166
    + 233

6. 546
    + 444

> We find the sum of two numbers by adding them.

 10b   Using Part-Part-Whole Bar Models in Addition

Solve. Draw part-part-whole bar models to help you.

Problem: My bar model:

1.   10
    + 20

2.   50
    + 40

3. 600
    + 100

4. 300
    + 500

10c Adding 10 and Subtracting the Leftover Ones

— Example —

42 + 9 = ?
Add 10 instead of 9.
42 + 10 = 52
The difference between 9 and 10 is 1,
and 52 − 1 = 51.
So, 42 + 9 = 51.

You can add 10 and then subtract the leftover ones to help you do mental math.

Do mental math. Add 10. Then subtract the leftover ones.

1   73 + 8 = ?

73 + _____ = _____

83 − _____ = _____

So, 73 + 8 = _____.

2   35 + 9 = ?

35 + _____ = _____

_____ − _____ = _____

So, 35 + 9 = _____.

3   88 + 7 = ?

88 + _____ = _____

_____ − _____ = _____

So, 88 + 7 = _____.

Explain why adding 10 and then subtracting the leftover ones makes it easier to do mental math. Use these words to help you write:

place   changes   count   back

_____

_____

_____

10d   Adding 10 and Subtracting the Leftover Ones

Do mental math. Add 10. Then subtract the leftover ones.

1   353 + 8 = _____

2   267 + 9 = _____

3   436 + 7 = _____

4   825 + 8 = _____

5   919 + 9 = _____

6   543 + 9 = _____

7   662 + 9 = _____

8   158 + 8 = _____

9   238 + 7 = _____

10   886 + 8 = _____

 10e   Adding 100 and Subtracting the Leftover Tens

Example

245 + 90 = ?
Add one hundred instead of ninety.
245 + 100 = 345
The difference between 90 and 100
is 10, and 345 − 10 = 335.
So, 245 + 90 = 345.

You can add 100 and then subtract the leftover tens to help you do mental math.

Do mental math. Add 100. Then subtract the leftover tens.

1   376 + 80 = ?

376 + _____ = _____

476 − _____ = _____

So, 376 + 80 = _____.

2   682 + 90 = ?

682 + _____ = _____

782 − _____ = _____

So, 682 + 90 = _____.

3   447 + 70 = ?

_____ + _____ = _____

_____ − _____ = _____

So, 447 + 70 = _____.

4   526 + 90 = ?

_____ + _____ = _____

_____ − _____ = _____

So, 526 + 90 = _____.

5   392 + 80 = ?

_____ + _____ = _____

_____ − _____ = _____

So, 392 + 80 = _____.

6   263 + 70 = ?

_____ + _____ = _____

_____ − _____ = _____

So, 263 + 70 = _____.

 ## 10f   Adding the Ones, then the Hundreds and Tens

> **Example**
>
> 823 + 5 = ?
> Add the ones first: 3 + 5 = 8
> Now add 8 to the hundreds and tens:
> 820 + 8 = 828
> So, 823 + 5 = 828.

You can add the ones first to help you do mental math.

Do mental math. Add the ones. Then add the sum to the hundreds and tens.

1   457 + 2 = ?

450 + _____ = _____

So, 457 + 2 = _____.

2   691 + 8 = ?

690 + _____ = _____

So, 691 + 8 = _____.

3   335 + 3 = ?

_____ + _____ = _____

So, 335 + 3 = _____.

4   512 + 3 = ?

_____ + _____ = _____

So, 512 + 3 = _____.

5   134 + 4 = ?

_____ + _____ = _____

So, 134 + 4 = _____.

10g Adding the Tens, then the Hundreds and Ones

Example

612 + 50 = ?
Add the tens first: 10 + 50 = 60
Now, add 60 to the hundreds and ones.
602 + 60 = 662
So, 612 + 50 = 662.

You can add the tens first to help you do mental math.

Do mental math. Add the tens. Then add the sum to the hundreds and ones.

1 735 + 20 = ?

705 + _____ = _____

So, 735 + 20 = _____.

2 346 + 50 = ?

306 + _____ = _____

So, 346 + 50 = _____.

3 272 + 10 = ?

_____ + _____ = _____

So, 272 + 10 = _____.

4 619 + 80 = ?

_____ + _____ = _____

So, 619 + 80 = _____.

5 460 + 30 = ?

_____ + _____ = _____

So, 460 + 30 = _____.

6 521 + 40 = ?

_____ + _____ = _____

So, 521 + 40 = _____.

10h   Adding the Hundreds, then the Tens and Ones

Example

539 + 200 = ?
Add the hundreds first:
500 + 200 = 700
Now, add 700 to the tens and ones.
700 + 39 = 739
So, 539 + 200 = 739.

> You can add the hundreds first to help you do mental math.

Do mental math. Add the hundreds. Then add the sum to the tens and ones.

1 125 + 300 = ?

400 + _____ = _____

So, 125 + 300 = _____.

2 468 + 400 = ?

800 + _____ = _____

So, 468 + 400 = _____.

3 237 + 200 = ?

_____ + _____ = _____

So, 237 + 200 = _____.

4 581 + 100 = ?

_____ + _____ = _____

So, 581 + 100 = _____.

5 656 + 300 = ?

_____ + _____ = _____

So, 656 + 300 = _____.

10i Mental Addition

Fill in the blanks.

1 54 + 24 = _____

2 30 + 30 = _____

3 400 + _____ = 600

4 47 + 9 = _____

5 563 + 8 = _____

6 736 + _____ = 796

7 645 + 3 = _____

8 885 + _____ = 895

9 330 + _____ = 630

10 50 + _____ = 100

10j Using Place Value in Mental Addition

Give an example to explain how place value helps you solve addition problems mentally. Use these words to help you write.

tens   ones   hundreds   add   break up   numbers

_____

_____

_____

_____

11a Finding the Difference

Subtract the smaller number from the greater number to find the difference.

Solve.

1
```
   68
 − 26
```

2
```
   54
 − 38
```

3
```
   129
 −  25
```

4
```
   632
 −  59
```

5
```
   925
 −  87
```

6
```
   545
 − 523
```

7
```
   961
 −  93
```

8
```
   400
 −  25
```

9
```
   243
 −  37
```

10
```
   365
 − 324
```

11b Subtracting 10 and Adding the Leftover Ones

Example

75 – 8 = ?
Subtract 10 instead of 8:
75 – 10 = 65
The difference between 10 and 8 is 2.
Now add the leftover ones:
65 + 2 = 67
So, 75 – 8 = 67.

> To do mental math, subtract 10 and then add the leftover ones.

Do mental math. Subtract 10 first. Then add the leftover ones.

1 67 – 9 = ?

67 – 10 = _____

57 + 1 = _____

So, 67 – 9 = _____.

2 85 – 7 = ?

85 – _____ = _____

_____ + _____ = _____

So, 85 – 7 = _____.

3 26 – 8 = _____

4 74 – 9 = _____

5 53 – 7 = _____

6 44 – 8 = _____

7 31 – 6 = _____

8 94 – 7 = _____

9 63 – 9 = _____

10 86 – 7 = _____

11c Subtracting 10 and Adding the Leftover Ones

Do mental math. Subtract 10 first. Then add the leftover ones.

1 985 – 6 = _____

2 767 – 8 = _____

3 846 – 7 = _____

4 628 – 9 = _____

5 532 – 6 = _____

6 427 – 9 = _____

7 333 – 8 = _____

8 274 – 7 = _____

9 166 – 8 = _____

10 924 – 6 = _____

11d Subtracting 100 and Adding the Leftover Tens

Example

863 – 70 = ?
Subtract 100 instead of 70:
863 – 100 = 763
To make 100, remember that you added
30 to 70.
Now add the 30 to the difference:
763 + 30 = 793
So, 863 – 70 = 793.

To do mental math,
subtract 100. Then add
the leftover tens.

Do mental math. Subtract 100 first. Then add the leftover tens.

1 537 – 60 = ?

537 – _____ = _____

437 + 40 = _____

So, 537 – 60 = _____.

2 842 – 70 = ?

842 – _____ = _____

_____ + _____ = _____

So, 842 – 70 = _____.

3 925 – 80 = ?

925 – _____ = _____

_____ + _____ = _____

So, 925 – 80 = _____.

4 336 – 60 = ?

_____ – _____ = _____

_____ + _____ = _____

So, 336 – 60 = _____.

5 229 – 90 = _____

6 455 – 60 = _____

7 322 – 70 = _____

8 263 – 80 = _____

9 767 – 90 = _____

10 849 – 60 = _____

11e Subtracting the Ones, then Adding the Hundreds and Tens

Example

927 – 5 = ?
Subtract the ones:
7 – 5 = 2
Now add the leftover hundreds and tens:
920 + 2 = 922
So, 927 – 5 = 922.

To do mental math, subtract the ones first. Then add the leftover hundreds and tens.

Do mental math. Subtract the ones first. Then add the leftover hundreds and tens.

1 698 – 3 = ?

8 – _____ = _____

_____ + _____ = _____

So, 698 – 3 = _____.

2 246 – 5 = ?

6 – _____ = _____

_____ + _____ = _____

So, 246 – 5 = _____.

3 119 – 4 = ?

9 – _____ = _____

_____ + _____ = _____

So, 119 – 4 = _____.

4 327 – 6 = _____

5 888 – 4 = _____

6 457 – 3 = _____

11f　Subtracting the Tens, then Adding the Hundreds and Ones

Example

674 – 30 = ?
Subtract the tens:
70 – 30 = 40
Then add the hundreds and ones to your answer:
604 + 40 = 644

> To do mental math, subtract the tens first. Then add the hundreds and ones to the answer.

Do mental math. Subtract the tens first. Then subtract the hundreds and ones. Finally, add the leftover tens.

1　953 – 30 = ?

　　50 – _____ = _____

　　_____ + _____ = _____

　　So, 953 – 30 = _____.

2　846 – 20 = ?

　　40 – _____ = _____

　　_____ + _____ = _____

　　So, 846 – 20 = _____.

3　661 – 50 = ?

　　60 – _____ = _____

　　_____ + _____ = _____

　　So, 661 – 50 = _____.

4　532 – 20 = _____

5　477 – 60 = _____

6　758 – 40 = _____

11g Subtracting the Hundreds, then Adding the Tens and Ones

Example

424 – 200 = ?
Subtract the hundreds:
400 – 200 = 200
Now add the leftover tens and ones:
200 + 24 = 224

To do mental math, subtract the hundreds first. Then add the leftover tens and ones.

Do mental math. Subtract the hundreds first. Then add the leftover tens and ones.

1 393 – 200 =

300 – _____ = _____

_____ + 93 = _____

So, 393 – 200 = _____.

2 674 – 300 =

600 – _____ = _____

_____ + 74 = _____

So, 674 – 300 = _____.

3 712 – 400 =

700 – _____ = _____

_____ + 12 = _____

So, 712 – 400 = _____.

4 855 – 100 = _____

5 499 – 400 = _____

6 548 – 200 = _____

11h **Rounding to the Nearest Ten**

To round a number to the nearest ten, see if it is closer to the ten below it or the ten above it.

Example

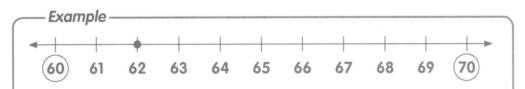

The number line shows that 62 is closer to 60 than to 70.
So, 62 rounded to the nearest ten is 60.
Numbers with 5 in the ones place always round to the ten above it.

Circle the tens place in each number. Then round the number to the nearest ten.

1   45   _____   2   27   _____

3   531   _____   4   58   _____

5   22   _____   6   366   _____

7   474   _____   8   82   _____

9   96   _____   10   99   _____

11   157   _____   12   263   _____

11i Checking for Reasonableness

You can round answers to see if they are reasonable.

Solve. Round each number to the nearest ten. Then add the numbers to check if your answer is reasonable.

1   347 + 221 = _____

_____ + _____ = _____

Is your answer reasonable? Why or why not?

_____

_____

_____

2   599 – 366 = _____

_____ + _____ = _____

Is your answer reasonable? Why or why not?

_____

_____

_____

11j Real-World Money Problems

Draw a bar model to help you solve. Show your work and check your answer.

Donna and Tina saved $456 altogether. Tina saved $345. How much money did Donna save?

My bar model:

My work: My check:

11k Money

Use these words to help you write a word problem about the things in the pictures.

cost   in all   sold   more   less   much   altogether

My word problem:

_____

_____

_____

Trade problems with a partner. Solve your partner's problem. Check each other's work when you both have finished.

My bar model for my partner's problem:

My work:

12a   Writing Fractions

You need to know two things to write a fraction:
1) The **denominator** is the number of equal parts in the whole.
2) The **numerator** is the number of shaded parts of the whole.

— *Example* —

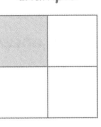

One out of 4 equal parts is shaded.
So, the fraction is $\frac{1}{4}$.

The shaded part, or 1, is called the numerator.
The whole, or 4 equal parts, is called the denominator.
We use the fraction $\frac{1}{4}$ to describe the shaded part of the whole.

Write the fraction that describes the shaded part of each whole.

1
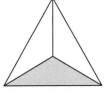
_____

2

_____

3
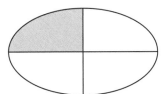
_____

4
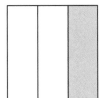
_____

Divide the rectangle below into 2, 3, or 4 equal parts. Shade one or more parts to make a fraction. Then fill in the blank.

My fraction is _____.

12b Comparing Fractions

Write the fraction each model shows.
Compare the fractions. Circle the
fraction that is less.

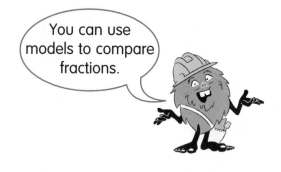
You can use models to compare fractions.

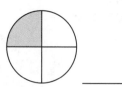 ____   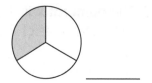 ____

How do you know which fraction is less? Use these words to help you answer
the question:

compare   less   smaller   part

_____

_____

 12c Comparing Fractions

Write the fraction each model shows. Compare the fractions. Circle the
fraction that is greater.

 ____   ____

How do you know which fraction is greater? Use these words to help you
answer the question:

compare   more   bigger   part

_____

_____

12d Ordering Fractions

You can use models to help you order fractions.

Order the fractions from least to greatest.

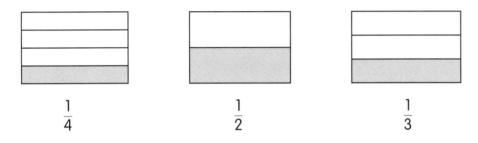

$\dfrac{1}{4}$ $\qquad\qquad$ $\dfrac{1}{2}$ $\qquad\qquad$ $\dfrac{1}{3}$

From least to greatest, the fractions are:

———— , ———— , ————

How do models help you compare fractions? Use these words to help you answer the question:

parts   whole   fractions

_____

_____

_____

12e Adding Like Fractions

┌─ *Example* ─────────────────────────────┐

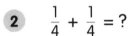

$\frac{1}{3} + \frac{1}{3} = \frac{2}{3}$

└──────────────────────────────────────┘

Fractions that have the same denominator are called **like fractions**. To add like fractions, add the numerators and keep the denominator the same.

Add.

1 $\frac{1}{2} + \frac{1}{2} = ?$

2 $\frac{1}{4} + \frac{1}{4} = ?$

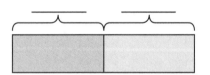

$\frac{1}{2} + \frac{1}{2} = $ _____

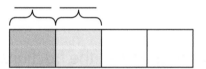

$\frac{1}{4} + \frac{1}{4} = $ _____

12f Subtracting Like Fractions

Write.

There are many real-life objects that can show us fractions. A pizza cut into equal parts is an example. Can you give some other examples?

_____

_____

_____

13a　Real-World Length Problems

Letters are used to stand for units of length.
For example:
　　　1 in = 1 inch
　　　1 ft = 1 foot/feet
Remember to read **1 ft** as in **1 foot** (**feet** if more than 1).

Draw a bar model to help you solve. Show your work. Then fill in the blank.

Bobby cuts a piece of paper 27 ft long to make a racetrack for his toy cars. He wants a longer track, so he cuts another piece of paper 14 ft long. He puts the two pieces of paper together. How many feet long is the new racetrack?

My bar model:

My work:

The new racetrack is _____ ft long.

13b   Real-World Length Problems

Draw a bar model to help you solve. Show your work. Then fill in the blank.

Bobby has a paper racetrack that is 32 ft long. He has another paper racetrack that is 11 ft longer. Bobby puts the two racetracks together. How many feet long is the new racetrack?

My bar model:

My work: My check:

The new racetrack is _____ ft long.

13c   Real-World Length Problems

Solve.

Maria has six pieces of wood. Each piece is 2 ft long.
Ronnie has five pieces of wood. Each piece is 4 ft long.

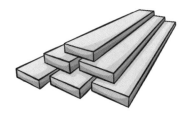

1   How many feet of wood does Maria have?

Maria has _____ ft of wood.

2   How many feet of wood does Ronnie have?

Ronnie has _____ ft of wood.

13d   Real-World Length Problems

Draw a bar model to help you solve. Show your work. Then fill in the blank.

Maria and Ronnie decided to use all of their wood to build a fence for their garden.
They have 11 ft more wood than they need to build the fence. How many feet of
wood do Maria and Ronnie need to build the fence?

My bar model: My work:

Ronnie and Maria need _____ ft of wood to build the fence.

13e   Real-World Length Problems

Remember to read **1 in** as **1 inch**.

Solve. Show your work. Then fill in the blank.

Sari has 7 rolls of ribbon of different colors. She cuts one piece of ribbon from each roll. Each piece is 5 in long.
Sari puts the pieces together to make one long ribbon. How long is the ribbon?

My work:

The ribbon is _____ in long.

13f   Adding Lengths

Add. Write the correct unit in your answer.

1.
```
   32 ft
+  83 ft
```

2.
```
  652 ft
+  28 ft
```

3.
```
  396 in
+ 477 in
```

4.
```
  25 in
+ 39 in
```

5.
```
  451 in
+  84 in
```

6.
```
  199 ft
+ 799 ft
```

13g The Importance of Facts

Why is it helpful to know your facts when you are solving a word problem? Use these words to help you answer the question:

know   problem   addition   subtraction   multiplication   division
words   quickly

_____

_____

_____

_____

Trade work with a partner. Discuss each other's ideas.

14a Skip-Counting by 5s on a Clock

You can skip-count by 5s to help you tell the time.

Skip-count by 5s. Write the numbers to match the minute marks on the clock.

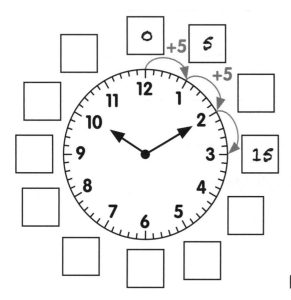

How many minutes are there in 1 hour? _____

14b Skip-Counting by 5s

How does skip-counting by 5s help you tell the time? Use these words to help you answer the question:

multiply   skip-count   numbers   minutes   represent
five   time

_____

_____

_____

14c Counting On or Counting Back to the Hour

Count on or count back to draw the hour and minute hands.

1 1 hour after 12:00

Time: _____

2 2 hours after 4:00

Time: _____

3 1 hour before 12:00

Time: _____

4 2 hours before 7:00

Time: _____

5 1 hour after 10:00

Time: _____

6 2 hours before 3:00

Time: _____

14d Counting On or Counting Back to the Half-Hour

Example

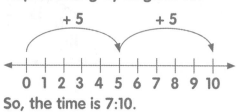

The shorter hand points a little after 7.
The longer hand points at 2.
Skip-counting by 5s gives 10:

$+5$ $+5$

0 1 2 3 4 5 6 7 8 9 10

So, the time is 7:10.

A clock's shorter hand shows the hour. Its longer hand shows the minute.

Write the hour. Then skip-count by 5s to write the minute.

1

Time: _____

2

Time: _____

3

Time: _____

4

Time: _____

5

Time: _____

6

Time: _____

14e   Real-World Time Problems

Count on or count back to draw the hour and minute hands.

1   30 minutes after 3:00

2   30 minutes after 8:00

3   30 minutes before 10:00

4   30 minutes before 11:00

 14f   Skip-Counting to Tell Time

Draw the hands on the clock. Then fill in the blanks.

Ailing finished her homework at 4:30. She went outside to jump rope for 1 hour. Then she spent 30 minutes eating dinner. What time did Ailing finish her dinner?

Ailing finished her dinner at _____, or _____ o'clock.

 **14g Time**

Use these words to help you write a time problem:

starts   finishes   time   hour   minute

My problem:

_____

_____

_____

_____

_____

Trade problems with a partner. Solve each other's problems. Discuss your answers when you both have finished. Your partner may use the empty clock face to solve the problem you wrote.

My partner's answer:

```



```

15a Drawing Equal Groups to Multiply by 3

Think of equal groups when you multiply.

Fill in the blanks.

1

5 groups of 3 = _____ groups with _____ balls in each group

5 × 3 = _____

2

4 groups of 3 = _____ groups with _____ balls in each group

4 × 3 = _____

3

3 groups of 3 = _____ groups with _____ balls in each group

3 × 3 = _____

15b   Skip-Counting by 3s

You can skip-count to help you multiply.

Skip-count to multiply. Fill in the blanks.

1

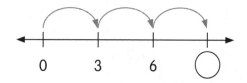

0   3   6   ◯

3, 6, _____

$3 \times 3 =$ _____

So, 3 skips of _____ is equal to _____.

2

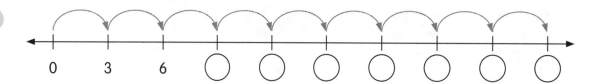

0   3   6   ◯   ◯   ◯   ◯   ◯   ◯   ◯

3, 6, _____, _____, _____, _____, _____, _____, _____,

$9 \times$ _____ $=$ _____

So, _____ skips of _____ is equal to _____.

3 $6 \times 3 =$ _____   So, _____ skips of _____ is equal to _____.

4 $7 \times 3 =$ _____   So, _____ skips of _____ is equal to _____.

5 $8 \times 3 =$ _____   So, _____ skips of _____ is equal to _____.

6 $5 \times 3 =$ _____   So, _____ skips of _____ is equal to _____.

15c Using a Dot Grid to Multiply by 3

— Example —

2 rows of 3

3 rows of 2

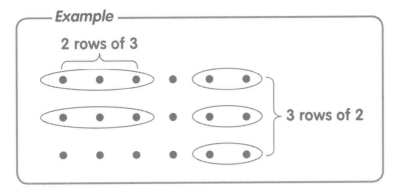

Multiply. Use the dot grid to help you.

1   4 × 3 = _____   3 × 4 = _____

2   5 × 3 = _____   3 × 5 = _____

15d Skip-Counting to Multiply by 3

— Example —

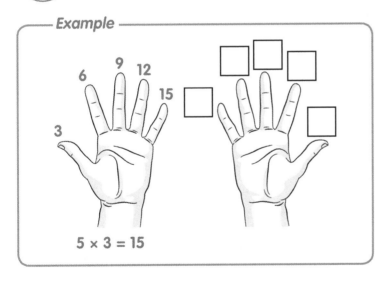

3

6

9   12

15

5 × 3 = 15

You can use your fingers to help you multiply.

Skip-count to multiply.

1   6 × 3 = _____

2   3 × 4 = _____

3   7 × 3 = _____

4   2 × 3 = _____

5   3 × 10 = _____

6   9 × 3 = _____

7   3 × 5 = _____

8   1 × 3 = _____

9   3 × 3 = _____

15e Skip-Counting to Multiply by 3

Skip-count to multiply.

1 $5 \times 3 =$ _____

2 $3 \times 1 =$ _____

3 $4 \times 3 =$ _____

4 $3 \times 3 =$ _____

5 $3 \times 5 =$ _____

6 $3 \times 2 =$ _____

7 $3 \times 3 =$ _____

8 $0 \times 3 =$ _____

15f Skip-Counting to Multiply by 4

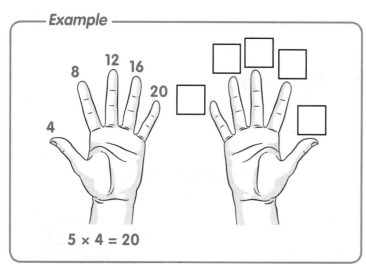

Example

$5 \times 4 = 20$

Skip-count to multiply.

1 $4 \times 1 =$ _____

2 $3 \times 4 =$ _____

3 $4 \times 8 =$ _____

4 $9 \times 4 =$ _____

5 $6 \times 4 =$ _____

6 $4 \times 7 =$ _____

7 $8 \times 4 =$ _____

8 $10 \times 4 =$ _____

15g   Skip-Counting to Multiply by 4

Skip-count to multiply.

1   5 × 4 = _____

2   4 × 1 = _____

3   4 × 3 = _____

4   0 × 4 = _____

5   4 × 4 = _____

6   4 × 2 = _____

7   1 × 4 = _____

8   2 × 4 = _____

 15h   Using Dot Grids in Multiplication

Multiply. Use the dot grids to help you.

1   4 × 2 = _____

2   2 × 4 = _____

3   3 × 2 = _____

4   2 × 3 = _____

15i Using Dot Grids in Multiplication

Multiply. Use the dot grids to help you.

1 3 × 3 = _____

- • • • • • • •
- • • • • • • •
- • • • • • • •

2 2 × 2 = _____

- • • • • • • • •
- • • • • • • • •
- • • • • • • • •

3 4 × 4 = _____

- • • • • • • •
- • • • • • • •
- • • • • • • •
- • • • • • • •
- • • • • • • •

4 5 × 4 = _____

- • • • • • • • •
- • • • • • • • •
- • • • • • • • •
- • • • • • • • •
- • • • • • • • •

15j Related Multiplication and Division Facts

> **Example**
>
> 4 × 3 = 12   So, 12 ÷ 3 = 4.

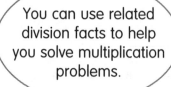

You can use related division facts to help you solve multiplication problems.

Complete the multiplication fact.
Then write the related division fact.

1 3 × 3 = _____   _____ ÷ _____ = _____

2 4 × 4 = _____   _____ ÷ _____ = _____

3 2 × 4 = _____   _____ ÷ _____ = _____

4 3 × 2 = _____   _____ ÷ _____ = _____

15k Related Multiplication and Division Facts

Write a multiplication fact and a related division fact.

1 Multiplication fact: _____ × _____ = _____

2 Related division fact: _____ ÷ _____ = _____

How does knowing related facts help you solve a multiplication or division problem? Use these words to help you answer the question. Draw a picture to go with your answer.

solve   multiplication   division   groups   same

_____

_____

_____

16a   Equal-Parts Bar Models in Multiplication

Example

2 groups of 3 = 2 × 3 = 6

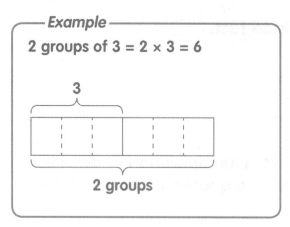

You can use bar models to help you solve multiplication problems and show your thinking.

Match the phrase with the correct bar model.

1   3 groups of 4

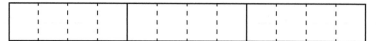

2   4 groups of 3

3   2 groups of 4

4   4 groups of 2

5   3 groups of 2

6   3 groups of 3

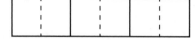

Draw bar models to help you solve.

My bar models:

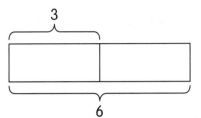

Example:

$2 \times 3 = 6$

7 $5 \times 3 =$ _____

8 $3 \times 5 =$ _____

9 $2 \times 5 =$ _____

10 $5 \times 2 =$ _____

16b Equal-Parts Bar Models in Multiplication

Draw a bar model to help you solve the problem. Show your work. Then fill in the blanks.

Cherokee bought 4 boxes of balloons for a party. Each box cost $4. How much did Cherokee pay for all of the balloons?

My bar model:

My work:

Cherokee paid $_____ for the balloons.

Related division fact: $_____ ÷ _____ = $_____

16c Equal-Parts Bar Models in Division

Example

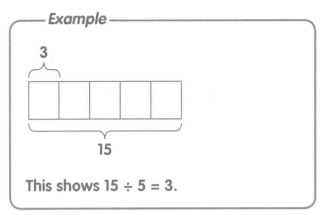

This shows 15 ÷ 5 = 3.

You can use bar models to help you solve division problems and show your thinking.

Write a division fact for each bar model.

1

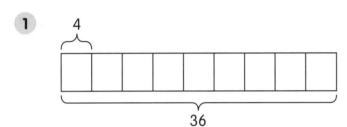

_____ ÷ _____ = _____

2

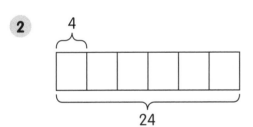

_____ ÷ _____ = _____

3

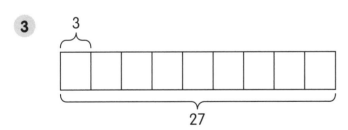

_____ ÷ _____ = _____

4

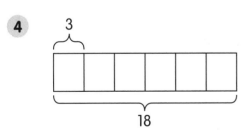

_____ ÷ _____ = _____

16d   Real-World Problems

Draw a bar model to help you solve and to show your thinking. Show your work. Then fill in the blanks.

Six students need straws for an art project. The teacher has 18 straws. He gives an equal number of straws to each student. How many straws does each student receive?

My bar model: My work:

Each student receives _____ straws.

Related multiplication fact: _____ x _____ = _____

 16e   Multiplication and Division

Multiply or divide.

1   5 × 4 = _____   **2**   2 × 3 = _____

3   3 × 5 = _____   **4**   10 × 2 = _____

5   4 × 3 = _____   **6**   25 ÷ 5 = _____

7   9 ÷ 3 = _____   **8**   12 ÷ 3 = _____

9   16 ÷ 4 = _____   **10**   8 ÷ 2 = _____

16f Multiplication and Division

Use these words to write a multiplication or division word problem:

group   equal   in all   each

_____

_____

_____

_____

_____

Trade problems with a partner. Draw a bar model to solve your partner's problem. Discuss your work when you both have finished.

My bar model for my partner's problem:

My work:

17a   Picture Graphs

Use the picture graph to answer the questions. Show your work if needed.

Number of Cut-Out Shapes in the Math Box

Triangle	Circle	Rhombus	Hexagon
△	◯	◇	⬡
✂✂✂ ✂✂	✂✂✂ ✂	✂✂✂	✂✂✂ ✂✂✂

Each ✂ = 2 shapes

Use the key to find out how many objects a picture in a picture graph stands for.

1   How many hexagons are there? _____

2   How many triangles are there? _____

3   How many rhombuses and circles are there? _____

My work:

4   How many triangles and circles are there? _____

My work:

5   How many hexagons and rhombuses are there? _____

My work:

17b Real-World Problems with Picture Graphs

Use the picture graph to answer the questions. Show your work if needed.

Number of Cut-Out Shapes in the Math Box

Triangle	Circle	Rhombus	Hexagon
△	◯	◇	⬡
✂✂✂ ✂✂	✂✂✂ ✂	✂✂✂	✂✂✂ ✂✂✂

Each ✂ = 2 shapes

1 How many hexagons and triangles are there in all? _____

> My bar model: My work:

2 How many more hexagons than circles are there? _____

> My bar model: My work:

17c Real-World Problems with Picture Graphs

Use the picture graph to answer the questions. Show your work.

Number of Steps Climbed by Three Children

Corrine	☆ ☆ ☆ ☆ ☆
Natalie	☆ ☆ ☆ ☆ ☆ ☆
Jen	☆ ☆ ☆

Each ☆ = 5 steps

1 How many steps did Natalie and Corrine climb altogether? _____

My work:

2 How many more steps did Corrine and Jen climb altogether

than Natalie? _____

My work:

3 How many fewer steps did Jen climb than Natalie? _____

My work:

17d   Real-World Problems with Picture Graphs

Use the picture graph to answer the questions. Show your work.

Number of Pet Visitors to a Pet Salon

Monday	Tuesday	Wednesday
♡ ♡ ♡ ♡ ♡ ♡	♡ ♡ ♡ ♡ ♡ ♡ ♡	♡ ♡ ♡ ♡ ♡

Each ♡ = 3 pets

1   How many pets visited the salon on Monday? _____

My work:

2   How many more pets visited the salon on Tuesday than on

Wednesday? _____

My work:

3   How many pets visited the salon on Monday and Wednesday

altogether? _____

My work:

17e Multiplication and Division

Multiply or divide.

1 2 × 2 = _____

2 1 × 9 = _____

3 0 × 10 = _____

4 6 × 5 = _____

5 8 × 4 = _____

6 45 ÷ 5 = _____

7 32 ÷ 4 = _____

8 4 ÷ 4 = _____

9 12 ÷ 2 = _____

10 21 ÷ 3 = _____

11 0 ÷ 3 = _____

12 30 ÷ 5 = _____

17f Picture Graphs

Draw your own picture graph. Give it a title. Include a key.

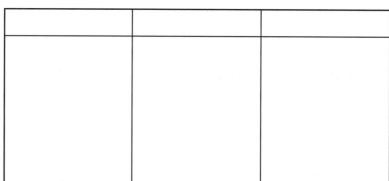

Title: _____

Each: ◯ = _____

Complete the sentence.

Knowing my multiplication facts helps me read and understand picture graphs

because _____

_____

18a   Groups of Sides

Fill in the blanks to complete the multiplication sentences.

Count the shapes. Then count the sides of each shape. How many sides are there in all?

1

_____ × _____ = _____ sides

2
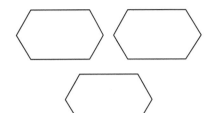

_____ × _____ = _____ sides

3
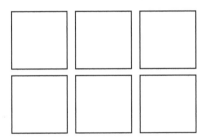

_____ × _____ = _____ sides

4

_____ × _____ = _____ sides

5
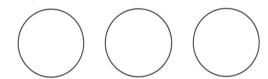

_____ × _____ = _____ sides

6
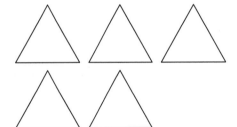

_____ × _____ = _____ sides

18b   Groups of Corners

Fill in the blanks to complete the multiplication sentences.

Count the shapes. Then count the corners on each shape. How many corners are there in all?

1

_____ × _____ = _____   +   _____ × _____ = _____

So, _____ + _____ = _____.

There are _____ corners in all.

2

_____ × _____ = _____   +   _____ × _____ = _____

So, _____ + _____ = _____.

There are _____ corners in all.

3

_____ × _____ = _____   +   _____ × _____ = _____

So, _____ + _____ = _____.

There are _____ corners in all.

18c Real-World Problems

Draw a bar model to help you solve. Show your work and check your answer.

Genevieve counted 789 flat surfaces in her home. Susan counted 599 flat surfaces in hers. What is the difference in the number of flat surfaces in their homes?

My bar model:

My work:

My check:

The difference in the number of flat surfaces is _____ .

18d Number Sentences

Fill in the blanks to make number sentences. Do not write the answers.

1. _____ + _____ = _____

2. _____ − _____ = _____

3. _____ × _____ = _____

4. _____ ÷ _____ = _____

5. _____ + _____ = _____

6. _____ − _____ = _____

7. _____ × _____ = _____

8. _____ ÷ _____ = _____

Trade problems with a partner. Solve each other's problems. Check your work when you both have finished.

19a   Faces

Example

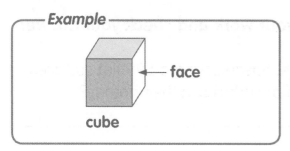

face

cube

Each flat surface on a solid shape is called a **face**. A cube has 6 faces.

Write multiplication facts to help you solve.

1   How many faces are on 1 cube?

_____ faces × 1 cube = _____ faces

2   How many faces are on 10 cubes?

_____ faces × 10 cubes = _____ faces

3   How many faces are on 4 cubes?

_____ faces × 4 cubes = _____ faces

4   How many faces are on 5 cubes?

_____ faces × _____ cubes = _____ faces

5   How many faces are on 3 cubes?

_____ faces × _____ cubes = _____ faces

6   How many faces are on 2 cubes?

_____ faces × _____ cubes = _____ faces

19b   Faces

Example

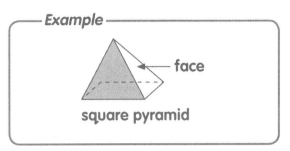

face

square pyramid

The bottom of a pyramid is called its **base**.
The base of this pyramid is a square. The other faces are triangles.

Write multiplication facts to help you solve.

1 How many faces are on 1 pyramid?

_____ faces × 1 pyramid = _____ faces

2 How many faces are on 10 pyramids?

_____ faces × 10 pyramids = _____ faces

3 How many faces are on 4 pyramids?

_____ faces × _____ pyramids = _____ faces

4 How many faces are on 5 pyramids?

_____ faces × _____ pyramids = _____ faces

5 How many faces are on 3 pyramids?

_____ faces × _____ pyramids = _____ faces

6 How many faces are on 2 pyramids?

_____ faces × _____ pyramids = _____ faces

19c Patterns

Draw the next two shapes in the pattern.

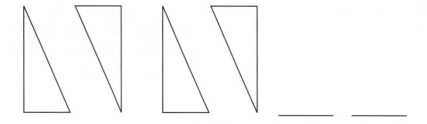

Mary wants to figure out an easy way to count the corners in the triangles above. Write a multiplication sentence that will help her.

_____ × _____ = _____

19d Faces

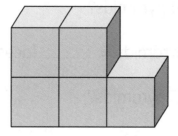

1 **Fill in the blank.**

Tino thinks that the cubes in the picture have a total of 10 flat faces. Is Tino correct? _____

2 **Write a multiplication sentence and a division sentence to explain your answer.**

_____

_____

_____

19e   Real-World Problems

Draw bar models to help you solve. Show your work. Check your answers if needed. Then fill in the blanks.

Erin drew 567 straight lines and 325 curved lines in her art book.

1   How many lines did Erin draw in all?

My bar model: My work:

Erin drew _____ lines in all.

2   Erin erased 47 lines. How many lines does she have in her art book now?

Bar model:

My work: My check:

Erin has _____ lines in her art book now.

19f Related Multiplication and Division Facts

Fill in the blanks to write related facts.

1   2 × 3 = _____

   _____ × _____ = 6

   6 ÷ _____ = _____

   _____ ÷ 2 = _____

2   8 × 3 = _____

   _____ × _____ = _____

   _____ ÷ 8 = _____

   _____ ÷ 3 = _____

3   7 × 6 = _____

   _____ × _____ = _____

   _____ ÷ 7 = _____

   _____ ÷ _____ = _____

4   9 × 4 = _____

   _____ × _____ = _____

   _____ ÷ _____ = _____

   _____ ÷ _____ = _____

19g The Importance of Facts

How does using facts help you add and subtract? Use these words to help you answer the question:

fact families   place value   doubles   checking   regrouping
tens   ones   hundreds   solve   word problems
drawing

_____

_____

_____

_____

_____

19h The Importance of Facts

How does using facts help you multiply and divide? Use these words to help you answer the question:

related facts   skip-counting   dot paper   checking
solve   equal   drawing   using facts to solve problems
word problems   groups

_____

_____

_____

_____

BLANK